LIVING ON THE EDGE

Michael Kelly is familiar to tabloid newspaper readers via his front page photographed meetings with Princess Diana and the Duchess of York. He writes a tri-monthly column about his experience of living with AIDS for *The Universe* newspaper, and independently launched a successful £35,000 appeal for a new lift at the Mildmay Mission Hospital in East London.

LIVING ON THE EDGE

An experience of AIDS

MICHAEL KELLY

MarshallPickering

An Imprint of HarperCollinsPublishers

Marshall Pickering is an Imprint of
HarperCollins*Religious*
Part of HarperCollins*Publishers*
77–85 Fulham Palace Road, London W6 8JB

First published in Great Britain
in 1993 by Marshall Pickering

1 3 5 7 9 10 8 6 4 2

Copyright © 1993 Michael Kelly

Michael Kelly asserts the moral right to be
identified as the author of this work

A catalogue record for this book is
available from the British Library

ISBN 0551 02749 5

Set in Imprint by Avocet Typesetters, Bicester, Oxon

Printed and bound in Great Britain by
The Guernsey Press Co. Ltd, Guernsey, Channel Islands

This book is dedicated to
those infected and affected
by HIV and AIDS

ACKNOWLEDGEMENTS

To my friend Claire who through all the ups and downs has kept a steady head to make sure I finish the book. To all my family, friends and support workers for caring and to Sarah for all the finger tapping.

CONTENTS

ONE

❦

A New Beginning

I don't remember leaving the consulting room. I don't recall walking those long hospital corridors. And the swing doors might never have existed. Yet the next thing I know I'm standing outside on the pavement, leaning hard against a brick wall.

It was five o'clock in the afternoon and Marsham Street, which was normally filling up with traffic at this time, was uncannily quiet. I searched feverishly in both directions. But there wasn't a lorry in sight. Just as well. Someone must have been watching over me.

I looked up. There wasn't a cloud in the sky, but then it was a warm summer's day. And yet I was shivering. I closed my eyes and tried to make sense of it all. HIV. Human immunodefi . . . I opened them in a panic. Did it mean I wasn't normal anymore? I remembered how people who had cancer used to become outcasts. Now I was an outcast. But why? Why did it have to happen to *me*?

A sense of anger and injustice flooded my mind. I thought back to my childhood and how difficult it had been sometimes for my Mum to make ends meet. I'd always tried to be a decent person, I reasoned, and done what was right, yet had still suffered for it in some way or other. Hadn't life dealt me a bad enough deck as it was, without delivering the ace as well?

Fragments of sights and sounds floated in and out of my consciousness as I stood there. Flashbacks from my youth mingled uneasily with the overwhelming impact of my diagnosis. The recent scaremongering in the press came to mind uninvited – lots of people shouting warnings about a disease they knew little about. Remembered phrases from these articles jostled for space with the blur of people passing me by, but I never saw their faces, just screaming headlines and accusing newsprint. Cold comfort for me. HIV, HI bloody V. It was as if all those stories had contributed to my condition, willed this to happen, come back to haunt me.

I was alternating between fear and anger, and rapidly losing control. Everything was becoming distorted, and panic finally consumed me. Would there ever be a cure? Had something gone wrong with the test? They must have got things mixed up. How could they do such a thing? Damn lies, all of it. It can't be me . . . can it?

Aghast at the implications, I imagined myself being shunned, despised, ridiculed, attacked. The pictures I drew in my mind were frighteningly real, but the sound of heavy braking jolted me back to reality.

It was the bus. Relief! Ten minutes earlier I'd have jumped in front of it. I chose a seat to myself, but the freedom of space I so desperately needed was short-lived. I stole a sideways glance at the woman who'd dared sit next to me. I then stared straight ahead, rigidly uncomfortable and aware that my breathing was frequent, shallow, and somewhat audible.

Would she notice? Was I giving myself away? I found myself hating her just for *being* there. I felt trapped. Everything started crowding in on me — fears, worries, sadness, a whole range of emotions — all heightened to fever pitch by the devastating news I'd received.

One minute I was full of remorse. The next I felt alarmingly wicked. I wondered what this woman would do if she knew I had HIV. Probably run off screaming! Should I tell her? Whisper it in her ear, perhaps? I laughed quietly at the idea, then felt thoroughly ashamed of myself. It was a nervous reaction, that's all. I was, quite simply, terrified.

I continued to stare straight ahead and, pursing my lips in my confusion, realized how painful they felt. I'd been biting them so hard I'd drawn blood. Quick! Wipe it away before anyone notices and gets frightened. After all, I've got HIV!

On the tube home I told myself that I must stay away from people, that I'd have to isolate myself in order to protect myself as well as other people. There was a great deal of uncertainty over how HIV and AIDS could be transmitted and, although I was sure that ordinary social contact posed no threat whatsoever, I didn't want to take any risks. And I had an over-whelming fear of being attacked. In occasional moments of lucidity I was aware that my thinking was muddled and my behaviour erratic. Clarity of thought and rationality of behaviour could wait another day, thank you!

Back in my flat I headed straight for my bedroom and crawled under the duvet, still fully clothed. Physically I was safe and unscathed. I'd escaped attack, thank goodness. The journey home had been nightmarish.

But the mental anguish intensified. Without any breathing space, the same questions and fears returned with renewed clamour, accompanied by others, previously untackled, for good measure. How would I tell my family, my friends? How would I find the courage to tell them? Would they reject me or show me their support? I had no answers, so the questions continued to bombard me from all directions. They assumed a power all of their own, got a grip of me, totally controlled me. I wondered if I'd ever be able to cope with day-to-day life again.

I remained under my duvet for most of that evening. I saw no one, spoke to no one, did nothing except drown myself in a relentless tide of self-torment. Horrified at the thought of having to go to work the next day, I finally settled down, exhausted, my eyes stinging, my head aching, my mind in turmoil. I didn't sleep at all.

Working nine to five the next day was a struggle, devoid of any sense of familiar routine. Jobs that had once been second nature to me were now huge obstacles to climb over and I wasn't sure of the route. I couldn't concentrate and made mistake after mistake. It was hard enough to cope with watching the clock move laboriously round to five o'clock, without actually being expected to do any work in between.

The normally conscientious, quick, efficient me was wilting. Had anyone at work realized? Perhaps they just thought that I was upset about something (well, I was), and that it would soon sort itself out (well, it wouldn't).

Perhaps they didn't notice. Perhaps they didn't care enough to notice.

But, then again, perhaps they did. Once they found out I'd got HIV, would I lose my job and end up on the scrapheap? Become an unemployment statistic *and* an outcast? I felt like giving up there and then.

I left at five o'clock precisely, not a second later. I couldn't get out quickly enough. By the time I flopped into my car, cold sweat was pouring off me. I was sinking, but I had to carry on. I *had* to work, to bring in a salary to live on. Otherwise, who knows, I might be homeless, out on the streets, and I couldn't bear the thought of that – *not in my condition.* "Keep striving, don't give in," I told myself in a rare moment of sanity.

I drove home, suddenly sick with worry over how I'd tell my Mum. I'd remembered she was going to ring me that evening. It had been the longest 24 hours of my life.

TWO

Before the Bombshell

Life before had seemed so simple . . .

It was five o'clock on Friday and the weekend feeling was rapidly approaching. I was the only one left in the office. I'd let my staff go home an hour early. The car hire business had certain peak demand periods during the year but the last two weeks in May was not one of them. When business temporarily hit the brakes and needed an injection of new trade, I encouraged everyone to participate in the process, and they had capitalized on a couple of uneventful days by working flat out to identify new customer outlets.

It was good experience for them. I believed in developing my staff and they rose to the challenge. I reflected on how rewarding it had been to see everyone leaving the office, praise proverbially ringing out of their ears and feeling they had made a very significant contribution to the company.

I took another look at my watch, aware that I should be heading home myself, since I'd invited friends around for dinner. There seemed little point in hanging around any longer when I could be working much more productively in my kitchen. I gathered up my papers, switched off my computer, found my keys, turned off the lights and was locking the door . . . when the telephone rang.

After a brief moment of hesitation and with a wry smile on my face, I went back inside and answered it. "Mike," said a voice I knew well. "Delighted you're still here. Listen, something's cropped up and I need a car in the next half hour. A two litre would be perfect. You can do it, can't you?"

Ross Charters was one of my best customers and needed no self-introduction. He was chairman of a large investment company in the City of London, but lived locally in a rather palatial residence in Buckhurst Hill. Despite the obvious trappings of wealth, including a Jaguar and a Land-Rover, both with personalized number plates, he preferred to hire a car for business-related affairs. I knew how much he appreciated the courteous, efficient service my company always extended to him and through personal recommendation he had referred several additional clients here for business.

"I'm sure that's no problem, Mr Charters. I'll have your car delivered right away," I assured him.

I had to act fast. I didn't want to disappoint him, despite the short notice and the knowledge that there wasn't a single two litre car available on the forecourt outside. I had in mind, however, a brand new Golf GTI I had acquired just three days earlier and which, after the weekend, was booked up for a solid eight weeks in advance. It would fit the bill perfectly. I even recollected Mr Charters hinting in the past that he'd always fancied trying out this particular model, but the opportunity had never presented itself. So that settled it.

I telephoned John, the supervisor at the garage, knowing he was due to lock up at any time, and asked him if he would come straight over to collect the necessary paperwork, then drive the car round to Mr Charters' home as part of a special service we'd agreed. He would then be able to collect a taxi from the main road for his journey back. The extra £4.50 cab fare was worth it. This was unexpected business on a car that would otherwise have remained in the garage.

Half an hour later I was behind the wheel of my own car, mentally racing through the menu I'd planned for the evening. I thanked God I'd made the carrot and coriander soup the night before.

Throwing a dinner party was not my favourite pastime – that spot was taken by my love of travel – but it would certainly have featured in my top three. I normally restricted invitations to dinner so as to make an easily manageable foursome, but on this occasion – an advance dose of midsummer madness I think I would have called it – I decided to be really energetic and push the boat out. We would be eight, the maximum number I had space for. Nights at my round table had never been so hectic!

I looked forward to all the detailed preparation such evenings entailed, though with me it was a very laid-back sort of organization, rather than any military precision. However, by the time I was answering the doorbell as friends arrived, things were generally well under control and I could ease off.

It was usually very informal, with long lazy pauses in between courses while the conversation grew steadily more intoxicating. The washing up would often be left until the morning – and why not; a man deserves a rest from the unpleasanter chores every now and then . . . so I'd lock up, switch off the lights, crawl into bed and fall fast asleep.

Meals out, on the other hand, tended to be arranged in a spontaneous, rather haphazard fashion and often at short notice. Seeing white space in my diary for the week ahead left me unperturbed because it would invariably get filled up. Friends would ring me at work and ask if I fancied going out to eat, and then I'd find myself in a restaurant that same evening.

There was a handful of restaurants, several of them Indian and relatively inexpensive, which could usually count on some business from me during the weekend. There's nothing better than a hot curry on a cold night . . . until, of course, the morning after.

There were also certain pubs I favoured and I used to frequent the odd jazz club, though I had no particular favourites. Ideally, the place would verge on the ever so slightly seedy – doubtless the dimly lit basement of an old establishment, somewhere with a bit of history. Mix an iced vodka and orange with a few renditions of the Cole Porter classics and I wish I could be there night and day. I never did find that dream venue!

Weekends were certainly precious to me and I liked to take full advantage of the opportunity they allowed to both relax and catch up with friends. My naturally outgoing personality seemed to attract a lot of people – for better or for worse – and it could easily have sounded like one heady round of socializing after another. But it wasn't like that at all. The trouble was,

I occasionally had to work on a Saturday and so my late soirées needed to be carefully planned. And although I had a wide circle of friends — some of whom I hardly ever saw from one year to the next — there were just a few special ones around this time whom I inevitably saw the most often.

Paul, for instance, who lived in Peterborough, and with whom the day would always be so wonderfully unstructured and carefree. We'd invariably go and visit some other city, but wouldn't decide where until we were actually inside the car. It was a case of "How do you fancy going to Norwich (or Leicester or Great Yarmouth) today?" followed by a chortle of approval, and off we'd go.

If I wasn't in London or Peterborough during the weekend, then you might have caught up with me in Birmingham visiting another friend, Peter, who had three adorable West Highland terriers. We used to chuck the dogs, their tails wagging excitedly, in the back of the car and drive to the Clent Hills. Their unrivalled location, to the south west of Birmingham, afforded magnificent views of the Black Country, the Cotswolds, the Malverns, and Kinver Edge. The best part of an afternoon was spent enjoying the fresh air and exercise, running around the National Trust parkland with the dogs and throwing sticks for them to chase until their weary little legs could cope no more. On the way home they simply curled up and went to sleep.

Stopping off to admire the countryside on my sorties from London became an eagerly awaited diversion (having been brought up in a small country village in Scotland), though I was always happy to return to the capital, the centre of things, the place which was my home.

I liked being so active, but at times I really did burn the candle at both ends until it started to hurt. Still, you're only young once. I was blessed with an abundance of energy, found I could easily make up for lost sleep, and wanted to capitalize on my good fortune.

Socializing apart, I also liked to devote some time to myself – personal space was very important to me – and to my flat. The value of keeping a home clean and presentable had been instilled in me at an early age (ace dish washer at ten; champion ironer at eleven) and borne out of necessity. My mother often lacked the time to do all the necessary household chores when I was young since she was out earning a wage to replace the money my father frittered away on gambling and drink. This conscientiousness around the home gave me a head start when I assumed my independence and had left Scotland to come and live in London at the age of seventeen. It meant that I was never embarrassed when anyone called unexpectedly. In fact, if I was disciplined enough, I could polish off the housework without having to sacrifice much leisure time at all.

My rise in the workplace typified how I was always striving for something better. When I was young I had had a father who never provided for his family and I wanted to prove that my upbringing was not going to be detrimental to me. Despite my childhood, I wanted to make something of my life. It was my way of righting some of those earlier wrongs which had caused untold suffering to the whole family. As long as I had food in the cupboard, enough heating, and a few savings to fall back on — just enough to be comfortable — I was happy. I appreciated the fact that I was able to have all these basics and tried never to take them for granted.

I was simply not interested in the artificiality of flaunting the financial side of things. I had known too much heartache come of it in the past. The get-rich-quick type buys a flash house and then sees his dream acquisition go up in smoke because, through mismanagement of money or by falling on hard times, he can no longer afford the new lifestyle he has created for himself. So, what little I had, remained my own private business. As for my accommodation, I was constantly on the move — a short let here, a short let there. The property-to-rent market seemed to thrive on short leases of life. Certainly in London it was the done thing. Yet I never found it tedious having to pack, unpack, and then pack again at such frequent intervals.

Having had to make do as a child with hand-me-downs and charity shop specials, I believed in spending some time and effort on my appearance. I remembered the hard times very vividly and as a result I was grateful that I was able to enjoy the well-made clothes I had only been able to dream about in my youth. Basically, I didn't have to count every penny when I went out shopping.

These were good times, and I seemed able to enjoy them all the more owing to my good health. A visit to my GP was a very rare occurrence, the only exception being for consultations over some recurring discomfort in my left ear. Despite the prescribed treatment, it never seemed to completely clear up. "Just one of those things," I used to tell myself . . . and then promptly forget about it until the next time.

Of course, I would suffer from the usual minor ailments every now and then as everyone does, but when you're otherwise healthy, they're not a problem and you just shrug them off.

In fact, it took a lot to get me down. I had the tendency (infuriatingly, many would say) to laugh off any problems in one way or another. I suppose I must have been the happiest, most easy-going person I knew. I was basically very ordinary — the boy-next-door type, I suppose — and I'd willingly help people out in any way I could. More fool me, sometimes — I'd take on more than I bargained for! My Mum often used to remark on how my innocent face would get me into trouble. She was right!

THREE

The Summer that Left Me Cold

I think it must have been some kind of conspiracy. If anyone needed a favour doing, the response always seemed to be "Ask Mike".

I was clearing up after lunch one Saturday afternoon when the doorbell rang. It was Pauline, an old friend of mine. "Aren't you ready yet?" she joked, with a certain air of impatience. "I've just got a bit of tidying up to do. Make yourself a coffee and I'll be with you in a minute."

We were taking part in a Fun Day in Epping Green, organized by the company I worked for. I'd been looking forward to it, though wasn't quite sure what to expect.

Having met up with a few others on arrival, I was enjoying a drink with them in the bar when a colleague came up to me, wearing that permanently etched smile of his that he used whenever he wanted something. He must have decided this was as opportune a moment as any to ask me.

"We're one short for the cricket team, Mike," he said ominously. "Do you want to join in?" I grimaced at the idea, not having played for years, but he had asked in such a way that I could hardly refuse. It was a Fun Day after all.

"So how about it, Mike? Can we count you in?" he asked with gentle insistence.

It seemed I had little choice.

"Yes, OK then. Cricket's not really my game, you know, but I'll give it a go. I only hope you know what you're letting yourself in for!"

"Oh, don't worry. I'm sure you'll be fine. You'll enjoy it! Team spirit — that's what it's all about."

It had rained overnight, which meant that the pitch had received a thorough soaking. The wet, muddy conditions made running between the wickets extremely hard going — you had to think of it as a challenge. I quickly entered into the spirit of the day and came off at the tea interval actually enjoying the experience. Once everyone had been fortified by a couple of pints of the clubhouse's best, we went back to the pitch, eager to get some early wickets, but conditions were now even worse in the outfield. The bowling had remained tight throughout, but then the spinner accidentally delivered a loose one and the batsman hooked it high and fast in my direction.

Realizing this would be the best chance I'd get to make any mark on the scoreboard, I ran like the clappers to catch it, but forgot just how soft the ground was. I slipped and fell flat on my back, caked in mud. I missed the ball, which made a boundary. My less than heroic attempt naturally raised a few laughs around the ground. So *that's* what they meant by a Fun Day! From behind I ended up looking like a rugby player. The match had been played in good spirits, however, and I didn't mind making a dirty spectacle of myself. It would all come off in the shower anyway.

But oh, those after-effects! I woke up on Monday, somewhat worse for wear. My legs were stiff, my back ached and I was developing a less than attractive collection of bruises. All from having fallen so spectacularly two days earlier!

I arrived at work to be met by everyone teasing me about the incident. But for me it didn't stop there. The accident seemed to trigger off a series of minor ailments. A cold, a throbbing head, and a sore throat plagued me for the next few weeks. And there was no noticeable improvement in my aching legs. I'd never had such problems in the past, but for some reason I was finding it difficult to shrug them off this time. Maybe I had incurred more damage than I realized.

I started to get rather concerned about it. My workmates made me think I was a hypochondriac and so I delayed seeing my doctor. I thought I just needed extra time, and that it would all go away and I would soon be back to normal. Maybe I was just being far too impatient.

Then my ear trouble flared up again, more painfully than ever before. The memory of the cricket match was rapidly losing its appeal. I was constantly cupping the palm of my hand over my ear in agony, which did not do much good, but it seemed a natural response to the unrelenting stabbing and discomfort.

"I think I ought to see my doctor about it all," I confided one morning to Frank, who, in terms of years, was the most senior member of the company. He was about the only one at work who had never made light of my injuries. I had played safe in my choice of confidant, since I wasn't in the mood for pleasantries this time. Frank gave me the confirmation I was looking for. No doubt about it, this time I had to have it investigated properly.

I duly visited my GP, who did nothing for my state of mind by giving the distinct impression he was somewhat puzzled about the cause. He referred me to a specialist clinic for several investigations, including a blood test.

The mystery continued when it was announced that the results had proved inconclusive. Although they indicated the problem was related to my ear drum, there were signs of some secondary infection which needed further exploration.

So, a second opinion was recommended. For this I was referred to the Westminster Hospital where I was advised to have another blood test, one which would include testing for HIV infection, and for which I had to give my permission, albeit reluctantly. The very word HIV frightened me – the disease was still very much unknown territory – but I didn't think I had anything to be scared about. The tests were conducted without any form of pre-counselling.

Three weeks then elapsed, during which I carried on life as normal, until one morning an anonymous brown envelope landed through my letter-box. It contained a request from the Westminster Hospital's social worker to telephone her at the earliest opportunity to make an appointment. I was anxious as to why a social worker should need to see me when I had had no previous contact with her, and I called her without delay. My worries were compounded when

the appointment was scheduled for just a few days'
time. There was an air of urgency about it all.

I arrived at the hospital and reported to Reception.
"Oh, just a minute, Mr Kelly, I'll let her know you've
arrived." I was about to take a seat when someone came
towards me, muffled a few words I didn't quite catch,
but which I suppose masqueraded as some kind of
welcome, and asked me to follow her down the corridor.
So much for the personal touch! This was the social
worker who had contacted me. She might as well have
remained anonymous.

The pace quickened. "Who did you last have sex
with?" she said as she rushed me down the stairs to
the consulting room. The cold, stark questioning lapsed
into undisguised panic as she repeated the question a
second and a third time, fuelled by my silence. I'd had
enough of her clumsy interrogation. I suddenly got very
scared. "Just get me in to see the doctor," I blurted
out. No amount of planning could have prepared me
for what happened next.

In total contrast to the social worker, the doctor gave
me a warm smile and asked me to sit down and make
myself comfortable. "I'm pleased you could come at
such short notice, Mr Kelly. There are a few things
I'd like to discuss with you."

He then explained to me how the tests had confirmed
there was a problem relating specifically to my inner
ear for which treatment was advised.

"But I'm afraid they also reveal something else."

My stomach sank. My mind raced back to when I
was asked to have the HIV test. The consulting room
suddenly felt like a sauna. My clothes were sticking

to me and I felt moulded to the chair. I saw him look at me with some concern before he continued.

"The fact is, Mr Kelly, your HIV test came out positive."

❧

FOUR

The Storm Before the Calm

That night, lying in bed, I found my thoughts straying back to my childhood . . .

The curtains were closed in my bedroom, but there was a little gap at the top where they didn't quite meet and I could see it was getting light outside. My mother would be back soon. I was looking forward to that. She had a horrible job cleaning buses on the night shift to get the extra money she needed to buy food for me and my brothers and sister. Yet she never complained.

I was scared of my father. He was a good-for-nothing, a crook, always in trouble with the police. They used to knock at the door at all times of the day and night asking where he was. Being woken up in the middle of the night became a regular occurrence. We used to get dragged out of bed while the police searched the house. I was never really sure what they were looking for, but I expect my father did. And then when the police had left, he used to take his anger out on us. I think he hated us all. He was too idle to get a proper job and he used to spend all his social security money down at the betting office. He always gambled it all away, because he was a born loser who never learnt. It was all gone by the weekend and then he'd get into a violent temper. Today was Friday.

My mother told me not to worry about her going out at night; she had no choice. It wasn't much fun seeing the electricity and gas cut off and not being able to do anything about it. My father used to take away the bills, but he never paid them. We'd have to get the candles out and resort to boiling up kettles and pans of water on the fire for cooking and washing. We used to toast muffins round the fire so often they lost their appeal. What might normally be considered a teatime treat became a dull habit.

My mother had to work during the day as well. Her absence from the house was felt even more acutely by me during the school holidays. My other brothers and sister often used to be farmed out to relatives and I'd be left to face my father on my own. Although my mother used to leave a key so that I could get into the house if I needed to — my independence came at a very early age — I didn't always take advantage of the opportunity. The idea of being home alone, with the prospect of my father appearing at any moment in one of his terrible moods, chilled me to the bone. If I thought he was already inside the house I wouldn't go in at all. I'd go to friends' houses instead and if no one was in, I'd trundle off to the sweetie shop round the corner and chat to nice Mr Stewart behind the counter. He was a kindly, bespectacled old man and very tall — a gentle giant, in fact. Luckily, he always seemed to have plenty of time for me. When the time came for him to shut up shop I'd have to leave, of course, though seldom without a few penn'orth of gums or a little bag of mints to send me on my way.

Sometimes I used to escape the village altogether and

head for my Granny's on the bus. It was a fifteen minute journey, with plenty of ups and downs and it often used to take longer if the bus was packed or when there was ice on the road. I'm surprised no one was ever asked to get out and give the rickety old thing a push! Two more stops and I'd be ringing the bell to get off. I could always be sure of being met. My Granny had a lovely little dog called Kim, who used to appear like magic at the bus stop to bark a welcome at me when I arrived – whatever the time of day. His sixth sense was generally rewarded with a little tin of Pal. And that, in essence, was what he was!

My Granny – or Wee Sadie as she was affectionately known – always gave me a warm welcome too. Small in stature she may have been, but she had a big heart.

Many a time Wee Sadie saved me from the unpredictabilities of my father. Her place was a refuge and a haven for me, because I knew my father would never be there. Although my granny was by no means infirm, she often used to ask me to do some shopping for her, which I really enjoyed. She was a canny woman and used to then present me with some of the tins and cakes I'd just bought on her behalf so that I could help fill the cupboard back at my own home. That way it was more like a "thank you" than a handout. It was all to do with pride.

By the time my mother eventually returned home from work and then cooked something to eat, very little of the evening remained. I used to get upset and go to bed at night feeling scared, wondering if it was all too much for her, especially since it was now the beginning of December and had turned very frosty.

One morning I thought I'd give her a nice surprise. I saw it was half past five and knew I had just about enough time. I sneaked down to the sitting room, trying not to wake anyone else (and especially not my father) and got together some paper, coal, and sticks in the hearth. I was going to light a fire for her, because she'd be cold when she got back in. I was just about to set a match to it when I heard raised voices outside the front door and the sound of someone trying to get in. I half closed the door to the sitting room and hid behind it as the people came into the hallway. I felt sick when I realized one of them was my father. I hadn't even known he was out. I wasn't sure who the other person was, because my father was doing all the swearing, but when I heard him tell the other person to get rid of those damn useless dogs because they always cost him money, I guessed it was probably Ron, a friend of his who raced greyhounds. It then went quiet so I thought they must have gone into the kitchen to have a beer.

I breathed a sigh of relief – they'd be in there for ages. I went over to the fireplace and picked up the box of matches again, but then sensed I wasn't the only person in the room. Hovering in the doorway was my father and his face was like thunder. He slammed the door against the wall, as if to leave me in no doubts as to his frame of mind. He staggered a few steps forward and asked me what the bloody hell I thought I was doing.

"It's for mum. She'll be freezin'," I spluttered, upon which his eyes pierced mine and his mouth opened in rage. He raised his right arm and gave me a good thumping for my trouble before telling me to get back to bed and not dare to make any more noise. But I'd only reached the bottom of the stairs when he was on my heels again.

"And what's this I hear about you quarrelling with that boy down the road?" my father yelled.

"B-But he threw my ball into someone else's garden and lost it. I got angry with him and he hit me."

Whenever he heard that I'd been involved in a fight he'd get it into his head to give me another beating for good measure and I'd end up suffering twice over, often for no fault of my own. It was all so unfair!

I looked into that cold, rough, menacing face of his. His eyes were strong and piercing and transmitted his scorn and contempt better than any words could. He was a bully, and I wouldn't have wished him on my worst enemy. As I looked him up and down, he towered above me and yet I suppose he was quite small really, especially compared to Mr Stewart at the sweetie shop. But one thing I did know was that he was as solid as a rock. I hated being close to him, because apart from the obvious threat of being hurt by him, he always smelled so horrible. My mother said it was stale beer and cigarettes. It had given him an ugly sort of greyish complexion. In fact, to me he was almost devil-like.

I dreaded what he'd do next. My eyes were on the verge of watering, but I hoped he hadn't noticed in his rage. I willed back the tears. I had to avoid crying in his presence. It wasn't worth it. He would have shouted insults at me and made me feel worse. I was too proud to give in. My cheeks and arms were beginning to sting with the beating I'd just received.

And, oh no, there was going to be more. He then proceeded to kick me up the stairs, every single step.

It didn't matter that I was crying out in pain for every kick he gave me. He just didn't care. I think he was enjoying it, the pig.

This wasn't the first time I'd been beaten up by him, but it was the worst so far. I collapsed into my bedroom, sore, bruised, and shattered. Even then he slapped me around some more while I lay huddled by the wall, but my pitiful pleas for him to stop seemed to increase his anger. They also alerted the friend he'd brought with him, whom I heard rush up the stairs. It *was* Ron.

"For God's sake, leave that child alone or you'll kill him." My father growled at him to clear off home, which, to my disappointment, he did, just like one of his greyhounds with his tail between his legs. Suddenly I was alone again with no one to defend me. I imagined my other brothers and sister nervously sitting on their bed, behind closed doors, not daring to move, not daring to think what was happening to me.

He shoved me hard against the wall. My nose was bleeding and my mouth had burst, splattering fresh red marks on the wallpaper behind me. Blood was also pouring down onto my pyjama top. Then he stood back, ripped off his belt, and I knew I was really in for it this time. I let out an agonizing yell as that rough leather strap seared across my face and opened fresh wounds.

On the verge of passing out, I bolted upright in bed, cupping my face in my hands. I was worried about getting blood all over the sheets. But there wasn't any blood, just cold sweat dropping off me. I looked towards the window. Instead of curtains with a gap at the top, there were blinds. I got up and looked at myself in the mirror.

I was 20 years older now and my so-called father had abandoned the family a long time ago. Time and time again I had wondered what kind of father could have done this to his son. It was a terrible memory to have relived and the nightmare had been horribly accurate in its detail. Everything was there, with nothing added and nothing taken away. But I was safe now. Then I remembered I had HIV and the nightmare began all over again.

As expected, my mother had rung me the previous evening. The conversation was somewhat strained. She started off by asking how I was, as she normally did. A harmless everyday question like this now had different implications for me. I took a while to respond, not knowing what to say. I just wanted to blurt it all out and get it over with, but, try as I might, I could not find the right words to tell her I had HIV. Everything was coming out jumbled. I'd start a sentence without finishing it and my voice betrayed my nervousness and fear.

I knew my mother must have been puzzled by my extended silences, and I am sure she sensed something was terribly wrong. But the courage to open up had become more elusive by the second. In the end I couldn't tell her, possibly because I hadn't really accepted it myself. I'd had a bad day at work, I said, which had left me with a stinking headache.

I may have extricated myself this time, but it couldn't go on forever. The constant cover-up would be too stressful. How many more people would I have to fob off with some paltry excuses? I was trivializing something serious. Yet it must have looked to other people as though I were exaggerating something trivial. If only they knew . . .

After tossing and turning with my thoughts all day long, I decided to keep my diagnosis a secret until I, Michael Kelly, was able to accept what was happening to my mind, to my body, to me.

In the next few days work carried on as before, although the extra spark I had injected into it was now missing. My social life almost came to a full stop. For a while all I did was go home and mull over the implications. I used to sit perched on the edge of the settee for hours on end, looking at nothing in particular, and feeling very uncomfortable, yet not having the inclination to do anything about it.

I came to realize that I needed help, and I started going to an HIV/AIDS support group, in the belief that my situation would improve if I talked things over with other people, especially people who were *strangers* with whom I had no emotional link.

But it didn't. On the first day I was due to attend, I deliberately kept putting off my departure until the last minute. When I eventually got to the meeting, fifteen minutes late, I was so unsure of what the outcome would be that I nearly turned back and headed for home.

Having entered the building, I was faced with four flights of stairs and no lift. I arrived, breathless, at the entrance to the room. The door was closed shut like a prison. There was no noise coming from inside. There was no sign of anyone or anything. I was shaking with nerves. It brought back a childhood memory of waiting outside the headmaster's study, fearful of the punishment to come. I wondered if this meeting would all be too much for me. I'd come here to try and be open about my feelings, yet my dry throat and clammy hands betrayed my discomfort and suggested I would be unsuccessful in my attempt. Unconvinced as to whether I was doing the right thing, I gulped a deep breath, pressed down on the handle and walked inside.

There were about fifteen people . . . and one empty chair. They must have known I was coming. I quickly slid into the chair and tried to become an invisible part of the group, rather than the late person whom no one could resist looking at. It created some tension at first, but I soon felt my confidence re-emerge. A quick glance around the room confirmed the group constituted a mixed bunch of people – men and women of all ages, some dressed casually, some smart.

Despite their external differences, they all shared one thing in common: their negative thoughts. It was something which I had noticed from the very first remark I heard and which continued throughout the discussion. I tried to liven up proceedings with frequent contributions to the conversation, but my comments fell on deaf ears. They heard me well enough, but never really listened to what I was saying.

I decided to give the group one more chance to work, and attended a second time, but it was the same story all over again. The record was well and truly stuck. It was non-stop doom and gloom – negative people with negative minds talking about death. It just exacerbated my personal situation and I was glad to be out of it.

Days, weeks, months went by in which I continued to live a very basic existence: nine to five during the day, with emptiness and loneliness at night. A wealth of opportunities lay outside — *Time Out* magazine said so! — but, closeted in my flat every evening, I effectively divorced myself from the world outside.

The questioning got worse. Why me? Has it all been a big mistake? I still hoped and prayed the doctors had got things wrong. I'd heard of new-born babies getting mixed up, so why not a couple of test-tubes?

And then I started getting pains in my chest. Fearful as to what this might turn out to be, I consulted my doctor at the Westminster. I had every faith in Adrian and quickly built up a trust in this eager, fresh-faced young doctor, although sometimes I saw the consultant who headed the department. AIDS had become the specialty of these two doctors, and Adrian was certainly keen to progress in his chosen field. After completing his medical check-up of me, he decided to refer me as a day patient to the Kobler Centre in Fulham, west London, so that more tests could be performed on me. An endoscopy was done, and it was discovered that I had oesophageal candida. My worst fears were now realized: I had an AIDS diagnosis.

I felt that after this, there could be no turning back. I had to take advantage of this new-found courage quickly, not knowing how long it would last. So I picked up the phone that evening and spoke to my sister.

"Hi Lorraine, I've got something to tell you." I paused. "I've got AIDS . . ." whereupon I broke out into nervous, uncontrolled laughter. Quickly pulling myself together again, I repeated calmly, in case she had not heard properly, "I've got AIDS."

This time there was an excruciatingly long pause. I just didn't know how my sister was reacting on the other side of the phone. "Just, just don't tell my mother," I said. "I *have* to speak to her myself."

There seemed little else to say. I felt too empty to continue the conversation. The silences had been very hurtful. I expected that this would be the taste of things to come. The thought of rejection stabbed me hard, like a knife in the back.

I took a day off from work to go and see my mother with the specific intention of telling her. The two hour drive to her place seemed to take forever, and I was sweating with panic, wondering what my mother would say. How *do* you tell your mother something like this? How would she react? She had already lost one son; would she now think she'd lose another? Would she disown me, or would she support me? Would she understand?

My mind inevitably wandered back to my younger brother. Edward had been tragically killed when he was just nineteen years old. He had been knifed on the street as he was going about his own business. The acute sorrow which enveloped my family was as painful in memory as it had been in reality. Would this open up all the old wounds for my mother?

Owing to the circumstances in which Edward had been killed, it had taken a long time for the police to release the body. Consequently, the funeral arrangements had to be delayed, and it was only when official clearance was given to go ahead that the grieving process could properly begin. Almost all my relatives came down from Scotland, including my father, who was not welcomed by anyone. My Auntie Mary cried her eyes out. It was she who had brought up Edward as one of her own, because my family had so often been split up when we were still children. It was the only way my mother could cope. As we were all standing around the graveside, with my father conspicuous in his solitude in the distance, I wished it were *him* going down! He had ruined his youngest son's chances the way he had squandered his own life through petty crime and drunken brawls, leaving no money to bring up his family properly. Edward had never been given a start in life.

With the image of my father imprinted on my mind, my hands instinctively tightened around the steering wheel. They could well have been around my father's neck for all I cared. As if in realization of the atrocity of my last thought, a cold shiver hurtled down my spine and I loosened my grip. The road ahead was suddenly presented to me as if for the first time. With my concentration having been completely haywire, I thanked God it was reasonably clear of traffic. No matter how strong my feelings against my father, I realized it was shameful to think in terms of such cold-blooded revenge. It had been a forced reaction, built up from a catalogue of injuries, abuses and insults over the years, but, even so, I was sorry. I calmed down out of necessity and renewed my focus on the remainder of the journey.

When I walked into my mother's house, there was not the usual warm greeting. Instead there was just a stony silence. And then, when she did finally acknowledge my presence, it was all very formal. I knew something had happened, but it didn't occur to me then that Lorraine had said anything to her.

We sat down on the settee. "So what have you been up to lately?" my mother asked.

"Oh, nothing much really. I've been kept busy at work, stayed in most evenings in fact. I've been feeling quite tired, actually."

"That's not like you," she said. "Usually you're tired because you're burning the candle at both ends."

"Maybe I've been overdoing it lately. Perhaps I just need a rest."

The conversation went on in this stilted way. I was hating every minute of it. When would I find the right moment to tell her?

In the end, I didn't have to. She just suddenly looked at me and said, "I know."

"What do you know?!" I asked in all innocence.

"I *know*. Lorraine told me."

I was stunned. I could have been spared the agony. I just didn't know what to do with myself. I had everything prepared in my mind and was just waiting for the right opportunity. Suddenly the carpet had been pulled from under my feet. My plan was in ruins, and the conversation was steering in a new direction.

"I've read about it in the newspapers," my mother continued, in an effort to fill the pause. Maybe she thought this would comfort me, but it was as if she was saying she didn't want to hear any more about it from me. She had virtually stripped me of a right to reply. I had no voice. And I didn't have the energy to argue. Not surprisingly, no further reference was made to it during the rest of the day.

I drove home feeling I'd achieved very little of what I'd set out to do. I didn't know if my mother really understood the implications. Hers was second-hand knowledge. Perhaps she had got some of the facts wrong. With a head full of worries and unanswered questions, and tormenting myself as to who to tell next, I went back to work carrying all these burdens, including the worst one of all . . . the AIDS diagnosis.

Over the next few weeks, things did not get any better. I needed to have some repairs completed on my flat and was outraged when I discovered that the builders knew I had AIDS. Not only that, but they were demanding to be issued with space suits, gloves and masks before they would even contemplate starting.

I had neither the time nor the energy to ascertain how they had found out about my condition. It made me feel vulnerable, threatened, at risk. I felt as though I was constantly looking over my shoulder.

In desperation, I contacted the Terrence Higgins Trust, who allocated me a counsellor. I looked forward to the opportunity to release my frustration and anxiety and arrived early for my first appointment. I was led into a small room with scatter cushions, which promoted a casual, relaxing environment. A cup of coffee was presented to me and after taking a few sips I felt confident to start opening up about the problems I was facing, which was rather unusual for me. The counsellor had a soothing voice and seemed to understand what I was going through, so I felt able to launch into some of the issues that had been troubling me. I spent a couple of hours in discussion with her, but it seemed like just ten minutes. I came out of the office feeling that a huge weight had been lifted off my shoulders. With more help like this, I could see myself pulling through. Perhaps things would improve from now on.

FIVE

A New Direction

The improvement was short-lived. Coping proved more difficult by the day. The effort of performing even the most essential of small chores was magnified out of all proportion. Brushing my teeth was a bore, making a cup of tea laborious in the extreme, and doing the dishes required a superhuman effort. Even getting out of bed was a hassle. *Everything* was overtaking me.

The spiralling downwards, like being on a never-ending helter-skelter, got stronger and faster and became so frightening that it took on hallucinatory images in my mind. I couldn't see any exit point. I felt imprisoned. The four walls were crowding in on me, suffocating the remnants of my existence. I couldn't go on like this. It had reached the stage where I was completely incapable of making a decision on anything. Life was ebbing away.

Sometimes the telephone would ring and I would just ignore it, in case someone was asking me to do something or to go somewhere. I didn't feel like making excuses. I just wanted to be left alone. If I hadn't needed to go to the local shops for milk and bread, I wouldn't have gone out at all. Having a bath was my highlight of the evening. I suppose it had something to do with being surrounded by liquid warmth and enjoying the sense of comfort and protection it afforded me.

I was due an outpatient's visit to the Westminster Hospital during this time. While waiting in the sitting room, Tina, my health adviser, came up to say that the consultant was running a little late. She had some time to spare and wondered if I fancied a cup of tea in her office. I accepted gratefully. She asked me how I was feeling, and I poured out to her all the problems I'd been having.

I saw her taking this on board, jotting down notes and generally assessing my situation. I was tired, lethargic, weak and had aches and pains all over my body, as if I had a permanent dose of the flu. I was aware she was asking me questions in the process, but I never seemed to get round to answering them or reacting to her in any way. I was on automatic pilot, endlessly bombarding her with information.

I stopped talking when I saw her put her pen down on the desk, sit back in her chair and just look at me. "What's wrong?" I asked. "What's wrong," she replied, "is that you need a rest. I'll see what I can sort out for you while you're in with the consultant. I'll give Mildmay a ring."

Mildmay's work in the AIDS field was already well known to me. A friend of mine had been a patient there, although I had never visited him. I knew the care was good, second to none, in fact. I remembered reading that it had been selected as the national model for AIDS hospice care, but I was a little suspicious about its Christian philosophy and how this was exercised. Just before it opened its first AIDS hospice unit in February

1988 (the first in Europe) questions had been raised as to whether it would force religion on its patients. The rumours seemed to fritter away to nothing. I'd come across no negative feedback since then and hoped that the lack of comment meant that the suspicions were unfounded. Anyway, it was a risk I was happy to take.

After seeing my consultant, I returned to Tina's office. She informed me that she had spoken to the admissions staff at Mildmay and would be happy to refer me to its AIDS Unit for respite care.

Everything then happened very quickly. A telephone call was followed by a visit from one of Mildmay's nurses to assess whether the referral for respite care was appropriate. He detailed the facilities Mildmay could offer and left me some literature to browse through, asking me to think about it over the weekend and ring back on Monday morning to confirm my decision.

I started reading up on Mildmay, digesting as much information as I could in an effort to be even better acquainted with its care, its services, its facilities, and its aims and philosophy.

The history of Mildmay was fascinating. I had no idea the work had started up as a Christian response to a cholera epidemic in London's East End back in 1866. The founder was the Reverend William Pennefather, affectionately referred to as "Holy Willie" by his descendants. He hailed from the Mildmay Park area of Islington, north London, from which the hospital gained its name. With the help of Florence Nightingale, this Anglican minister trained his deaconesses "to heal the sick and preach the gospel" to the people in the worst affected areas.

This all seemed very evangelistic to me, but reading through the rest of the literature, I was given no reason to believe that, in 1990, preaching to a captive audience was still the practice. However, the Christian element was obviously very important to Mildmay: it formed the backbone to all its work. It seemingly permeated the actual work by lending it an additional dimension – the care of body, mind *and soul*. Christian faith seemed to be translated into action. *That* was their Christian ministry. Well, I would soon have the opportunity to find out for sure.

The literature created a warm, welcoming impression, and so eager was I to be admitted that I got up early on the Monday morning, showered, had breakfast, dressed and waited until it was only just past nine o'clock before ringing the referral team at Mildmay. I was admitted on the Wednesday.

Feeling somewhat nervous, I didn't want to drive to Mildmay. But neither did I feel up to going on my own, even though I was living in Stoke Newington, only a short bus ride away. So I was grateful when my cousin Alice offered to come with me. It made me feel I wasn't on my own.

We were welcomed in Reception by one of the nurses, then travelled to Elizabeth Unit on the third floor in an old, noisy, industrial lift – which had me frowning in amused consternation at Alice. It seemed so outmoded. Inside the Unit, however, the décor was modern and tasteful in warm, pastel shades. I was shown my room, which had an *en suite* toilet and handbasin.

I looked at Alice, wondering what to do next. I sat down on my bed and found myself gazing through the open doorway. Seconds later I saw a patient walk by. He looked really ill and extremely frail. It frightened me. It made me think I was living on borrowed time — it was like a death sentence. Would I ever look as emaciated as this? I asked myself whether I'd done the right thing in coming here. To have seen someone in this condition, given my own state, was bound to strike a negative note. If the person had had Kaposi's sarcoma, a rare form of skin cancer which can affect people with AIDS and which reveals its presence by its often extensive purple blotches, well, that would have finished me off there and then.

Such manifestations on the skin also indicated a more serious spreading of the disease internally. The very idea filled me with fear. Looking emaciated is bad enough, but with AIDS you have to make the best of it. With Kaposi's sarcoma, though, you have no control. Pride in appearance can go tumbling out of the window.

Noticing the anxious expression on my face, as I continued to stare at the empty doorway, my cousin was quick to reassure me that everyone's needs were different, that I'd come here for a complete rest and that this was the best place I could be. Changing the subject slightly, she commented on how impressed she already was by the warmth of the atmosphere. So was I, in fact, and I was not to be disappointed.

After saying good-bye to Alice, I ventured out of my room to make some tea. I would unpack later. I was met by smiling faces, not doom and gloom, and it relaxed me. Shortly afterwards, I was introduced to the nurse who would be responsible for co-ordinating the care I would need during my stay. The ratio of nurses to patients is very high at Mildmay (two nurses to every three patients) and it was as if I had my own personal nurse on call 24 hours a day.

No time was lost in planning an individually tailored programme of care and support for me. Mildmay adopted a multidisciplinary approach – in which doctors, nurses, therapists, counsellors, welfare advisers, chaplains and other professionals work together *with* the patient to improve quality of life. I didn't need any specific medical input or symptom control, although I was in a mess physically and I did need to rest, relax, and recharge myself. Nor did I require any physiotherapy or occupational therapy. Counselling, however, was essential to help with my emotional and psychological state. Helpful sessions with Mildmay's senior counsellor, Shirley Lunn, quickly established the origins of my problems and therefore allowed me an opportunity to sort them out.

I was consulted at all stages of my programme and was offered various options. Since the care was very much self-directed, this gave back to me the sense of dignity and self-esteem which I had hitherto lost. I felt as though I had started assuming control again. It felt good.

I soon got chatting to the other patients and was relieved to find that not all the patients were "ill" with AIDS (a contradiction in terms, really) and were not all there for terminal care. At least half had been admitted for respite care, like me, and appeared to be reasonably well and coping successfully. It gave me renewed inspiration to live with my own condition.

The freedom and flexibility and encouragement of independence on the Unit suited me perfectly. The Unit was not a prison and in the interests of normality I liked to go out occasionally. One afternoon I went to the cinema in the West End with the patient whose appearance had caused me so much alarm shortly after I had been admitted to my room. His name was Simon and I felt drawn to helping him in his condition. I treated him to a pizza afterwards, and, judging by his reaction, a meal out was something he hadn't experienced for quite some time. He was due to be discharged in a couple of days to a new flat and he asked if I would go round to look at it with him. He wanted a second opinion. I decided that I'd keep in touch with him to make sure he was all right, since I was so much healthier than he was and, having a car, more mobile.

Although he was wary about leaving the comfort and warmth of Mildmay, his apprehension was overcome by his excitement over his new flat and the idea of regaining his independence.

Independence, in fact, was keenly encouraged all around me at Mildmay. Life "off the Unit" was positively promoted if you were well enough and it was facilitated by the supporting presence of a nurse or volunteer if you were not. The patient's wishes at Mildmay were always paramount and providing the journey was not ill-advised on health grounds, there were plenty of opportunities to get out and about, whether by personal or public transport, or even Mildmay's minibus.

Back on the Unit, the encouragement of independent living was an attractive feature. It wasn't a "lights out at ten and breakfast at nine" mentality. Nor, indeed, were bacon, eggs, and the Bible served for breakfast. There was no heavy evangelism at all. However, since I *was* in a state of spiritual turmoil, it was suggested I might like the opportunity to speak to Father Tim. I took up the offer.

Father Tim was no ordinary priest! (He didn't even look like one, which, as far as I was concerned, helped enormously.) He was an excellent listener. I kept asking him *why*. Why had I been struck down with AIDS? I told him that I felt as though I were being punished and needed reassurance and the spirit to fight on. In the gentlest of manners, Father Tim succeeded in putting my mind at ease. Through the unravelling and interpretation of my own thoughts, I convinced myself that God was still out there. I had been beginning to doubt it.

Mildmay soon made me feel I was part of a large family. The staff seemed really to care about you and were attentive to how you were feeling. There was an immediate response to calls for assistance or to concerns over any new pains and ailments.

I was also finding it helpful to talk to other patients and their families. There was an acceptance of my condition. There were no barriers to climb over and it wasn't just about AIDS that we talked. We exchanged a wide variety of beliefs and comments – information you wouldn't normally get to know about someone for a long time.

But I did have one complaint: the food. The dinner

was so awful one evening that I couldn't stomach any of it. Capitalizing on my active mood, I decided to do something about it myself, rather than complain to one of the nurses. I knew there was always a good supply of food in the kitchen on the Unit, in case patients chose to cook meals independently, so after a quick check, I donned an apron and got cracking with several boxes of eggs. I ended up cooking omelettes for half the patients who, incidentally, thought my antics hilarious, but who applauded them none the less in the form of some plain, some with mushrooms, some with smoked bacon, and others with melted cheese. "Omelettes various, coming up," I announced to the eager rattle of knives and forks on the dining table. Honestly, it was like being back at school again! Shame about the lack of tips . . .

One morning, the Unit's domestic, Josie — famous for her long flowing silver hair and strong Irish accent — surprised me with a steaming plate of porridge for my breakfast to accompany the fresh coffee she always made. It provided a welcome change from my normal selection of cereal and toast and reminded me of my schooldays when I used to dash downstairs on a cold winter's morning to be greeted by my mother pouring out this wonderful white concoction, which remained piping hot right to the last spoonful.

Amply nourished for the whole morning, I could only face a light lunch and then I took to the conservatory in the afternoon to listen to some Gladys Knight on my Walkman. This was an environment I felt very relaxed in, with its colourful array of plants, flowers, herbs and fountain. So relaxed, in fact, that

ensconced in my favourite armchair I promptly fell
asleep for several hours.

I had apparently been checked on at regular intervals,
but allowed to continue sleeping out of respect to my
body's natural responses. I'd been allowed to be *me*.

After a week's stay, the improvement in my condition
was almost tangible. After a fortnight, it was complete
and I was once again the strong, happy, life-loving free
spirit that I had been before, but that I had almost
forgotten about.

I'd had such a positive experience at Mildmay that
I was actually looking forward to going home. What
with hospital visits and the physical and emotional
exhaustion surrounding my AIDS diagnosis, I had
been off work for a month now, of which Mildmay
accounted for the last fortnight. I now needed to get
back into the work routine mentality – back to being
a Road Transport Coordinator for the Post Office.

Had I foreseen the dark clouds on the horizon,
however, I would have been reluctant to leave Mildmay
and the protection it had offered me.

SIX

Helping Myself and Helping Others

I was happy to be back in the flat that just two weeks earlier had caused me such misery. That was because I was now looking at things from a fresh perspective.

I had rediscovered an inner energy, a will and an enthusiasm to live, to really *live* again. It was an extraordinary change from the desperate condition I had known a mere fortnight ago when I arrived at Mildmay in a complete mess physically, mentally and spiritually. The care and attention they had lavished on me had made me look honestly at my life and my direction. After all, I was not so badly off compared to some of the other patients in there. Before I was admitted, I thought I was the only one with problems. But some of the other patients there had Kaposi's sarcoma, some had walking difficulties, some had gone blind, some were painfully emaciated and some had dementia-related conditions. I now realized that there were many more people going through the same situation, and much, much worse, but still managing to survive.

I now started to lavish more attention on my flat. I painted the kitchen walls daffodil yellow. When I applied the first few strokes I liked what I saw so much that I abandoned my plan to tackle the job in several stages and just carried on without a break until I had finished. The colour reflected a bright cheeriness, a *top of the morning* feeling which I hoped would last the whole day. When the sun shone through the window the effect was even more startling.

The new creation had tired me out, but given me immense pleasure. I kept going back into the kitchen to have a look, it gave me such a positive feeling. I would not have even contemplated decorating my kitchen pre-Mildmay, let alone done it.

I also noticed how my plants — spiders, rubbers, ferns and several other species — were thriving, promoting life and hope, consistent with the new me. Before, they had demanded to be watered, fed and cleaned like hungry young children and their maintenance had drained me.

A return to work beckoned. My employers, the Post Office, had become suspicious of the true state of my health during the time I was away and in confirmation of their anxiety, they sent me a letter to say that I would be receiving a visit from the Occupational Health Officer. This made me very nervous.

My mind flashed back to when I had left the car hire firm. My diagnosis had then been constantly playing on my mind, and my work had suffered. I had had to attend outpatient clinics and hospital appointments more and more frequently, and colleagues had become increasingly concerned and were asking rather pointed questions. I hadn't wanted their suspicions confirmed so had left my job to concentrate on sorting out my medical condition. After a few months of being at home I was mentally more capable of dealing with my condition, had stabilized medically and recharged myself, and was ready to venture back into work. The Post Office job had been the first I'd applied for.

Now I was feeling nervous all over again.

I couldn't keep saying I had a bad chest infection (even if I had) every time I was ill and needed time off, without specifying the underlying cause.

The doorbell rang and I was somewhat nervous at answering it, knowing it would be her. I went downstairs and invited her in. On the way back up I found myself in two minds. Shall I tell her? Or shall I keep quiet? I gave myself some more breathing space by offering her a cup of tea, which she happily accepted. I perceived little benefit in any further procrastination and decided to be honest about my condition.

I got straight to the point. "The long and short of it is that my illness is HIV-related," I said. Her response astonished me.

"Oh, you'll have to be careful on the tubes and trains now, travelling to and from work, won't you. You don't want to pick anything up." Her head was bowed, which I felt betrayed the insincerity of her remark and her weakness. She did not see the dirty look I threw at her. She inspired such little confidence, yet so much depended on her assessment of my situation. Her reaction was as cold as the tea which now pointedly remained untouched and which later had to be thrown down the sink. Had my employment chances also gone down the plughole?

I had been informed there would be a few days' wait while she compiled her report. My anxiety soared. I wondered how much I was being talked about behind my back, how much my situation was being discussed without my being there to defend myself. After all, were they really aware of what they were putting me through, of keeping me on a knife's edge? They must be, I thought, since they boasted about their equal opportunities policies. That must account for *some*thing. The questioning therefore stopped. My mind was put at rest. I had nothing to worry about.

I was duly summoned, in no uncertain terms, to attend an interview at the Head of Personnel's office in Croydon.

Obviously concerned about the latest turn of events I contacted my union representative and arranged to meet him for lunch in order to prepare for my interview. I knew from his reactions during the meeting, however, that it would be down to me to argue my case. He had no idea of the issues involved and could not appreciate the level of discrimination being shown by the Post Office against me for having AIDS. Yes, he was sympathetic, but it was the wrong kind of sympathy, born out of ignorance and he just ended up being hideously patronizing. I was mortified at his attitude and at times wondered whose side he was on. I'd paid my dues to the union and felt there was no support just when I needed it most. I wish I could have obtained a refund of all my union subs in protest at his incompetence.

Going into the interview, I felt I would now be fighting two people instead of one and the whole experience could have been extremely daunting. However, I was grateful for the pleasant and understanding approach the Personnel Officer took.

She may have hummed and ha'd quite a bit over whether I would be able to fit back in again — the other staff would not know the exact nature of my illness, but would obviously be aware that I'd been on extended sick leave — but at least she showed an awareness of the issues involved and wasn't cloying in her sympathy.

There were three options open to me: either I could have my job back, take a job share, or be given medical retirement. There was then a sudden silence in which I was made painfully aware that I had to give my response there and then. My mind was like spaghetti junction, except the criss-crossing of my thoughts did not find a ready exit! I could feel the seconds ticking away. But there was only one response I could give. Out of the jumble, I answered, as emphatically as I could, "I want to return to work." It then seemed an age before she gave her reply: that she would contact my consultant at the Westminster immediately. If he could confirm that I was fit to work, then I could be reinstated. She assured me that the matter would probably be resolved in a couple of weeks and this was agreed in the presence of my union representative who, by this time, I'd forgotten was sitting next to me.

I came away from the interview feeling I'd achieved something. The matter, though, was actually resolved in half the time. Imagine my disbelief when a week later I received a letter from the Post Office to say that discussions with the Occupational Health Officer had led them to believe I was *unfit* for work and consequently they had decided to retire me on medical grounds.

When I next visited the Westminster for my

outpatient's appointment, I raised the issue with my consultant, who angrily declared, "But they never even contacted me for a statement." In a show of extreme sympathy and in a more soothing voice, he continued, "It seems they never even gave you a chance, Michael."

I felt so embittered about the situation on my journey home that I decided to contact my union representative again. No prizes for predictability here . . . he advised me to accept the decision: appealing against it was unlikely to bring about change, he said. So much for the Post Office's much-vaunted equal opportunities policy. They had gone back on their word. I wondered who had instigated the final decision. I found it hard to believe it could have been the Head of Personnel, whom I had spoken to, so I suspected the director she reported to. *He* must have refused to back her up, vetoed her recommendation, I thought. The union, on the other hand, had hardly put in a single good word for me. They had wanted me to give up from the word go.

So, having emerged a couple of weeks earlier from Mildmay brimming with confidence and a new get-up-and-go philosophy, I was suddenly downcast and down-spirited. The future looked all too bleak. I was informed I wasn't entitled to a pension because I hadn't worked for the Post Office for long enough. All I received was a month's salary in lieu of notice . . . and my P45 which now amounted to a redundant piece of paper. It might as well have been a UB40! And, more sinister, obviously in the protection of their own interests, not mine, I was forced to sign the Official Secrets Act, which effectively stopped me from discussing the decision for twelve months.

Not only had I been put out of a job, but I had also been put out of the running for future jobs. A reference from the Post Office was out of the question. How could I apply for a job and quote the reason for leaving my last employment as "medically retired"? No one would be interested in employing someone who had been medically retired at the tender age of 31.

The sad thing was that I wanted to work. I wasn't finished. I wasn't a spent force, even though I had been made to look and feel one. All the good that Mildmay had brought me had been well and truly undone. The Post Office really didn't have a clue about the damage they had inflicted on me. As far as they were concerned, I was just a statistic in their personnel file and had already been conveniently filed away, probably in the archives.

And yet, incredibly, I later received an advice note recommending I transfer my pension payments to another scheme. What scheme? How could I transfer them when I'd been put out of the running for a job? I ended up cashing them in, for what they were worth, inevitably losing out on much of the value because they were nowhere near maturity.

There now seemed nothing to look forward to. No prospect of work. No structure in my life. I had visions of being stuck in my flat, surrounded by four walls, with my plants and everything else – even life itself – dying around me. I felt cheated. Cheated out of a chance to continue being a person. I no longer had a salary coming in. The bills were already piling up. Should I pay the gas and the electricity, and risk having my phone cut off? But, then, I couldn't because the phone was my lifeline. So then I'd either have to be cold, or go hungry, neither of which I relished. I wondered how on earth I would keep my head above water.

I was consciously denying myself an actual existence. I just wasn't interested in doing anything, going anywhere. Friends got the cold shoulder. Sally asked me to a party. I said no. David invited me to Brighton for the weekend. I said no. Brian suggested a few drinks at the pub up the road. I said no. "No" had become my favourite word. It was so much easier than saying yes, and having to make an effort to fight my lack of energy, purpose and motivation.

I was to suffer further degradation at the Department of Social Security, following their receipt of the form (of which I had received a copy) sent by the Post Office confirming I had been on sick leave and was being medically retired. An appointment was made for me to attend the local social security office to explain the details to them. I had no idea they would put me under such intense scrutiny. Throughout the interview I kept wondering whether my status would remain strictly confidential and I asked for this assurance. I kept looking around me, scared of being overheard. All this for just a few pounds a week more!

To add insult to injury, the first couple of Giro cheques went missing and I was left without money for a whole month. When I complained about never having received them, I was accused by the social security officer of lying. He said I would have to come into their offices and accordingly, for the second time in a month, I was summoned to a potentially very unpleasant interview.

Upon arrival I was treated like a criminal. "Guilty until proven innocent" was obviously their philosophy. There were no finer feelings here, for sure. I was literally marched into an interrogation room and sat down while some pitiful social security people played amateur detectives. Questions were asked. Answers were given. They alleged that I had already cashed the cheques and spent the money. This piece of fantasy enraged me and, bearing in mind my innocence, was treated with the contempt it deserved. They then changed course and suggested that maybe as a result of my condition I had forgotten that this is what I had done. It was starting to become ever so slightly confused. When I realized the despicable tactics being employed, I fought my corner even harder until there was nothing left to accuse me of. I felt as if I had been in a police cell, but the famous yellow and orange seat covers in shabby nylon gave away its true location.

It transpired that when the two cheques were returned by the Post Office, my signature had been forged in each instance, although it bore no resemblance to my own. I hoped the thief enjoyed spending the money because I'd been left without any at all. I was reduced to scrounging from friends for essential purchases and payments, and to living off a contingency supply of food that I'd saved for a rainy day. But this rainy day lasted for a whole month.

Aware of my changed circumstances, a support group invited me to run a self-help office for people with HIV and AIDS, based at Mildmay. The work would involve giving emotional and practical support to patients and their families, offering welfare advice, sorting out benefit entitlements and housing problems and liaising with charitable organizations that were able to provide one-off grants for special needs.

From having been made an unemployment statistic, I was suddenly in demand! It was the best possible thing that could have happened to me. I felt valued again, my sense of dignity and confidence reassuringly restored. Now I was ready to take on a new challenge.

I was thrilled at the thought of establishing closer links with Mildmay, this time as a provider instead of a user. Moreover, I enjoyed the idea of helping patients and their families, since I could now understand many of the issues and difficulties they faced. After all, it was often an extension of something I had already experienced myself, and I could consequently develop an easy rapport with them.

Furthermore, since I was no longer employed, I had plenty of time on my hands. Running a self-help office would therefore be a worthwhile way of filling up the day and give me a sense of purpose and a sense of structure again.

So I accepted.

I lost no time in organizing my new office to my own liking. Its location, just around the corner from Elizabeth Unit, which had cared for me, seemed very convenient in view of the nature of my work. And I soon found out that I would never be short of things to do.

One of my most frequent jobs entailed liaising with various agencies and persuading them to pay the bills that patients were not in a position to settle themselves. Ann-Marie, a regular on the day centre, presented me with her telephone bill one day and asked if I could help her out. She had gone through a bad period and had needed to use the telephone more frequently than usual to ring her doctors, her hospital, her friends, and her family. At such times the telephone is a lifeline. The bill was three times the normal size and she could not afford to pay it.

The first charity I approached was itself short of cash. "You know as well as I do, Mr Kelly, that we're all having to be careful how we spend the little money we have available, and the fact is we have nothing remaining in our special needs budget." It would have been futile to continue the conversation, apart from expressing the usual civility of thanks and the hope that I could approach the charity again with any other requests once their situation had improved. The next organization I approached was also experiencing a cash-flow crisis, but the grants officer referred me to a similar company he thought might be able to help.

So I tried again, this time successfully, though not without a bit of hard negotiation. I emphasized that payment of this bill constituted a one-off exercise in exceptional circumstances. What really swung the decision in my favour was the fact that the company had a policy of serving the local community, and Ann-Marie lived just a couple of streets away from them.

After some initial difficulty, I was also particularly pleased when I obtained payment of the mounting travelling expenses incurred by the family of a haemophiliac patient. They lived on the Essex coast and invariably travelled to Mildmay every day to see the father, only occasionally staying the night since there were children involved who needed to continue their schooling with the minimum of disruption.

The parts of the job I enjoyed the most, however, were when I drove patients to other centres and hospitals, and sometimes to special events. I took one patient, Brian, to see the Christmas lights in London's West End. He hadn't been feeling particularly well that day and I was told by the nurses that he took most of the afternoon to dress up for the occasion. The evening out was designed to boost his morale. We went in my car.

Thankfully, it had the required effect. We walked up and down Oxford Street, gazing at all the decorations *en route* and marvelling at all the window displays. We agreed that Selfridge's came out top, on account of its beautifully re-created snow scenes and grottoes. Brian's eyes were as bright as the illuminations themselves.

Soon after that, I was asked to accompany one of Mildmay's nurses on a home visit to a patient who used to attend the day centre. I remembered him as someone who spent most of the time on his own in a corner of the lounge, not wanting to join in with the others. Although whenever I saw him I tried to involve him in the conversation, he was never very willing and seemed terribly shy. Apart from making the occasional visits to Mildmay, he hardly ever went out the door. I thought that, in the familiarity of his own environment, he might be encouraged to open up a little more. Certainly I could see he was grateful to receive some news on the benefits he was entitled to claim – for this formed the basis of our visit – but he was frugal in his choice of words. Yet, shortly after this visit he accepted my invitation to take him one lunchtime to Body Positive's drop-in AIDS centre at Earl's Court. So it had been worth the effort.

Back at Mildmay, patients would often ask me to come and sit at their bedside and support them through their emotional problems. At other times they would invite me to have a coffee with them in the conservatory. They found it helpful to speak to another person with AIDS, and supposedly in the same situation, yet I invariably would leave their company feeling overwhelmingly guilty.

"But you look so healthy," they all used to say, as if they didn't believe I had AIDS. I repeatedly had to tell myself that it was wrong to feel guilty; after all, I was hardly wishing illness on myself. None the less, I found it difficult to contend with.

And what I found incredibly sad was that just as I'd build up some kind of understanding with patients who were really ill, they'd be gone. I felt though, that I'd achieved *something*, and I hoped that I had helped them in their last few days. The value I attributed to this overcame the guilt factor.

I was eager to develop my skills, and when the opportunity arose to attend a counselling course, I jumped at the chance. It was being run by the Project for Advice, Counselling and Education (PACE in short), which deals with HIV-related issues and anxieties. It trains members of voluntary organizations and health and local authorities, and runs in-house courses. It meant a commitment of a couple of hours every Wednesday evening for eight weeks. The course proved invaluable in giving me a deeper insight into helping people cope with problems and in improving my own listening and communication skills. There were sixteen of us, with a good cross-section of backgrounds and personalities, and all with a story to tell. The offload session at the end provided welcome relief in a safe environment. I was able to open up quite easily, and therefore went home reasonably relaxed.

As I became more widely known within Mildmay I was invited to take on an increasing number of speaking engagements which concentrated on my own experiences as a person living with AIDS. I gave talks to doctors, nurses and a wide range of other disciplines for Mildmay's Education Centre, either at Mildmay itself or in London teaching hospitals. I would address various aspects of service provision, my preference for a patient-directed model of care (which Mildmay operated so well), and the importance of trying to understand the issues faced by people with AIDS. I was also asked to speak to people involved in counselling and bereavement support projects. CRUSE, for instance, the national bereavement care organization which offers counselling, information and support to anyone, was receiving a growing number of requests to counsel friends and families of people affected by AIDS. In response, the organization needed to develop an improved understanding of the issues surrounding AIDS. I was invited along to its annual conference in Bedford one Saturday so that they could listen to my own story.

In volunteering my services, I was thanking Mildmay in my own way for what it had done for me: I wanted to repay some of the kindness. I was happy to extend the remit of my job simply because it was such worthwhile work. It was actually the start of a lot of things.

My time at Mildmay had made me feel part of the community and now I was able to put something back into it. Before, I had felt isolated. I used to stay in at home and, because of my sinking depression, find myself wallowing in my misery. From a feeling of emptiness and loneliness I had found a new direction. I started getting to know more people and could associate with them comfortably (rather than hide) and let my true self emerge (rather than be scared of being ostracized).

It was a major breakthrough! It told me I had accepted the illness for the first time, and life would start anew. I was spiritually healed, mentally healed, and physically reborn, almost. In fact, if anyone had told me I was fit enough to run in the London Marathon I would have had no difficulty in believing them. As it happened, it did cross my mind more than once to compete, but I had missed the deadline for the receipt of applications.

Still, there was always next year!

SEVEN

Up Front and in the Public Eye

6 February 1991

It had all the signs of being an ordinary sort of day.
I collected my mail, showered, had my cup of breakfast
tea, enjoyed several slices of toast and marmalade whilst
listening to Capital Radio, and drove through the heavy
traffic to Mildmay. I always used to try and arrive for
about eleven o'clock. People then knew when to expect
me. I went straight to the post room to see if there was
anything in my pigeon-hole and said a quick hello to
the nurses on duty on the way to my office.

At half past eleven I was expecting a visit from the
distressed mother of a patient who was very ill. She
was finding it difficult coming to terms with the
situation and was looking for some moral support and
encouragement. After all, she was just an ordinary
woman and had never experienced anything like this
before.

She arrived on time and I just let her have the
freedom of speech she needed. I was expecting her to
be really down, but with an opportunity of being able
to speak to someone she thought might understand, she
was in a much better frame of mind and gave full vent
to her feelings. I had to concentrate so hard at times

it was exhausting just being there. She left with her spirits raised. It was I who was left downcast. *C'est la vie!*

I thought ahead to the rest of the day and what I would have given for just a little bit of excitement. Since I wasn't expecting any more visitors, it seemed I would have to create something myself. Hoping for inspiration, I sat at my desk with my elbows propping up my chin and found myself staring at the door.

The sound of someone knocking at the door made me look up in surprise. Who would it be? "Come in," I said, and the door slowly opened to reveal a woman I'd not met before.

After introducing herself, she said that although we hadn't actually met, she knew a little about me, and about the work I was doing at Mildmay for which she thanked me. She went on to say that if the time was convenient, she'd like to spend a few minutes with me to discuss a VIP visit that was due to take place in a couple of weeks' time.

Things were looking up! There was an air of expectation and I was very, very intrigued to know more. I was not disappointed. The invitation really was as special as she had made out, and I felt honoured to have been asked.

I hardly dared believe what had happened in the space of just a few minutes. In comes a stranger, out walks a colleague and somewhere in between I had been invited to meet the Duchess of York at Mildmay in a fortnight's time in front of the Press.

Excited I most definitely was, but I had been well advised on the very public nature of it all. Would I be willing to promote myself as a person with AIDS? Indeed, it would be a brave decision to go public. My only previous press experience had been a short and fairly anonymous interview for the BBC World Service programme *Health Matters*. I remember being as nervous as an actor going on stage for his first night, except I wasn't acting. Seconds before the interview, however, I seemed to acquire an unshakeable confidence. Commenting on the care I had received at Mildmay, I felt truly inspired and my words and thoughts emerged with a clarity and a fluency which surprised me. One "take" was all that was needed. Despite the air of confidence, however, I was relieved when the interview was over, and I couldn't have spent a second longer in that room. I felt hot, sweaty and lifeless, and needed some privacy and some fresh air. I had never before realized that a seemingly simple interview could have taken so much out of me. But compared to what I might be about to undertake, this radio interview was merely a rehearsal — a sort of limbering up for the major exercise.

I took a deep breath and tried to steel myself up to the implications. Oh no, they seemed never-ending . . . My condition would no longer remain a secret to a privileged few; it would be reported in the press for anyone and everyone to digest. And people would see my face. It could leave me very vulnerable. One minute I was as excited as a young child with a new toy; the next I felt sick with apprehension.

But in going public I would have the opportunity to help other people with AIDS who didn't have the courage to talk openly about their condition and who, as a result, were forced to lead a lonely life, not of their own choosing, due to the ignorance of others. I might therefore hope that those who knew nothing about AIDS, and those who were misinformed, or prejudiced in their views, could be helped to a more compassionate understanding. After all, I would be putting a human face to the disease — a face that wasn't emaciated or scarred by the purple disfigurations of Kaposi's sarcoma. I wanted to provoke a positive reaction and realization from people: "But that could easily be my son, my neighbour, my workmate. I would never have known he has AIDS."

Although it was not an easy decision, I realized it was an opportunity I could hardly refuse. So an ordinary sort of day was transformed into an extraordinary one. But then, I hadn't counted on the arrival on the scene of Claire Wheatcroft, Mildmay's publicity manager . . .

For the next few days the invitation to meet the Duchess of York hardly escaped my every thought. One of my ambitions had always been to meet royalty, but I never dreamed I'd have such an opportunity. I simply *had* to accept. So I told Claire, who was delighted for me. And I immediately knew I'd made the right decision.

However my excitement during the last few days before the visit was made more containable by news of the depressing developments in the Gulf War, now receiving saturation news coverage. Consequently I realized that details of the royal visit, and hence my own exposure, would be greatly reduced and could even be squeezed out of the news altogether. I felt a little disappointed, but relieved all the same. Perhaps this was for the best. Some of the pressure was already off. Maybe I would now be able to enjoy the occasion more.

20 *February 1991*

The big day was finally here. I arrived at Mildmay in good health, in good spirits and in good time.

I met up with Claire who handed over to me a bouquet of roses, carnations, and freesias for the presentation. She wished me well and squeezed my arm with words of warm encouragement. With less than an hour to go before the scheduled arrival of the Duchess, she then left to welcome the Press and give them a briefing.

I decided to go up to my office and to sit down for a while, to be on my own with my thoughts. I was both excited and nervous at the same time. Eventually I got up and moved across to the window. As I looked out I saw a green Rover, complete with police escort, rolling down Hackney Road. It was the royal party! Not wishing to be late, I belted back downstairs. Even on a last minute visit to the bathroom I never let the flowers out of my sight!

In spite of all my inner preparation, it was still daunting to see all those reporters and photographers intent on covering the Duchess's first visit to an AIDS centre in this country. There would be much attention focused on her.

Although I didn't have a conversation prepared in my mind, I obviously did have an idea of the kind of things we might be able to talk about. As she walked down the corridor towards me, I took one last look at the flowers which, of course, were still in absolutely perfect condition. On presenting them to her, the battery of photographers flashed away and I was bathed in light. The Duchess was accustomed to all this, but I certainly wasn't!

She commented on the flowers' beautiful fragrance. "Were they sprayed with Givenchy?" she asked. "No, Yves Saint Laurent," I replied. The good humour was to continue throughout our long conversation, and I even commented on the delightful gold teddy bear brooch she was sporting on the lapel of her olive green suit.

The Duchess's bubbly personality and informal manner quite surprised me, and had the effect of making me feel completely at ease. There was also a serious side to her, evident when she looked at me and asked how I was feeling. She was friendly, relaxed, completely unhurried, commenting on how lovely it was here and on the warmth of the atmosphere. I couldn't help but agree and give my own views on Mildmay and how the respite care I received had given me a new direction in life and a desire to set new aims, embark on new projects. Nor could I resist mentioning Mildmay's lift at this point and how I longed to see it replaced by an easy-to-use fully automatic version. It was the worst thing about Mildmay, I said, and I was considering organizing some fund-raising for a new one. "Perhaps you could tell people about it on your travels," I joked. She said she would try and help in whatever way she could. Maybe we could have the lift sooner than we thought!

Once the Duchess had left, the Press were keen to do some follow-up questioning. It all went very smoothly until a reporter tried to attract my attention to ask me how I had contracted the disease, upon which he pretended to inject his arm with a syringe and carried on writing as if he had already answered his own question. He had already judged me, categorized me, labelled me in his own little guessing game. I was thoroughly disgusted and felt the anger surge within me. I looked at Claire who was ready to intercede on my behalf, but then I quickly regained my composure and my pride, looked him straight in the eye and said, honestly, in reply, "I have no idea. Does it really matter?"

I then turned around and focused my attention on the questions being asked by the local reporters in front of me. They were obviously keen to add more background information to the news articles they were preparing.

Soon after the royal visit the Roman Catholic newspaper *The Universe* telephoned Claire in response to the press information she had already issued. They had already decided to run a piece on the spiritual and emotional experiences of a Roman Catholic living with AIDS but were now persuaded to build this up, linked in with the royal visit, into a centrespread feature.

Claire gave me first option. I felt very privileged, but needed to think about it carefully. This was new territory for me! She had assured me that the motives behind the article were irrefutably sincere and consistent with what I was wanting to achieve, in terms of helping people to improve their understanding of the issues surrounding AIDS and their effect on people living with the disease. In fact, I admired *The Universe* for its brave stance in addressing AIDS at all, as it seemed to be such a taboo subject within the Roman Catholic community. It was certainly a risk, considering people's existing prejudices, and I anticipated some controversy of opinion among the readership. But I was ready for any confrontation. The determination to humanize the AIDS issue and to help people to an improved understanding spurred me on in the face of the personal pain and psychological suffering that tends to envelop one when emotions are laid bare. And so a date for the interview was settled: Thursday 14 March.

I arranged to meet the reporter from *The Universe* in Claire's office. I wanted to meet on neutral ground and have someone there for support, as I realized that a lot of soul-searching would have to be done. I delved back into my childhood on a number of occasions, dredging up memories and emotions long since buried.

I also addressed the sensitive issue of the need for Christians to respond to the growing AIDS crisis. I was in the mood for challenging misconceptions and uncaring attitudes and gave full vent to my opinions.

The reporter, who was taping the conversation, therefore heard how I believed that the Christian community – which is supposed to be an inherently caring community – should accept that the problem of AIDS is not suddenly going to disappear. I said that if I were still living in the very close Roman Catholic community I was raised in, I would have been "stoned" by now, purely because of the negative attitudes it bred. People would come to the door to show sympathy, but later they'd stick the knife in your back: a typical two-faced approach. As far as I was concerned, it was the duty of Christians everywhere to look behind the myths surrounding AIDS, which have mostly been created through ignorance. "As Christians we should not be judgmental," I said. "It doesn't matter which denomination we belong to. Who are we to judge anyway? We all lead less than perfect lives."

I breathed a heavy sigh of relief after the interview, but it wasn't until I was back home later that afternoon that the full emotional force of the interview hit me. And even this paled into insignificance compared to the effect the published article produced on me. Reading about yourself in print is quite another matter. Although I had seen the newspaper coverage and the extensive use of the black and white pictures of the Duchess of York and me following her visit, an in-depth feature, which reveals publicly for the first time so many personal details, goes much further.

The much-awaited edition of *The Universe* arrived on a Tuesday when I was at home. Claire rang me and I went in that afternoon, specially to read it.

The feature was high on emotion. There were no surprises in that. But what did take me unawares was the deep and uncontrollable effect it would have. Headlined *Brave Mike can stare AIDS in the face*, the article almost had us both in tears. I had to keep reminding myself it was *me* the reporter was writing about. And taking pride of place in the feature was a large colour photograph of me in conversation with the Duchess.

I drove home in a state of semi-shock. The reality

of events was suddenly proving very painful. Right at
this moment, I certainly could *not* stare AIDS in the
face. Once inside my lounge I threw myself onto the
sofa and allowed the pent-up emotions to burst free;
the hot tears stung my red-rubbed eyes. When I could
cry no more, I simply lay exhausted, dizzy almost, from
the effort of it all. I stared blankly at the walls and
ceiling, lacking the energy to do anything else.

I wondered what my relatives in Scotland would
make of it, as they could easily pick up a copy on their
way to Sunday Mass. For some it would be the first
they knew of my condition. Naturally I was concerned
at their reaction and, indeed, at how the Roman
Catholic community in general would respond. Would
it now be a case of sitting back and waiting for the
reaction of the readers? Would there be nasty letters
– crank mail, perhaps? Or would there be messages of
support?

I tried to exercise some kind of control over what
came into mind, but without success. Against my will,
I found myself thinking of Edward, my brother, once
more. I should never have mentioned my brother in
the interview, but I had, and now I regretted it. It was
a memory I could never erase. To have resurrected the
old emotions may have been a freeing, releasing
mechanism for some, but for me it weighed very heavily
on my mind. I vowed not to mention this part of my
past again to the press.

It was a private tragedy not intended for public
consumption.

Despite these after-effects of opening up for *The
Universe*, I allowed a succession of interviews to follow,

including involvement in a religious documentary on AIDS care for ITV and a programme for cable TV asking me about the spiritual aspects of the care I had received at Mildmay. It was becoming easier to bare my feelings on the issues surrounding AIDS although I was careful not to overstep the parameters I had set. Some things were just too personal to talk about under the public gaze. But I considered it an honour to give one unconditional endorsement of Mildmay after another.

Then one morning out of the blue I received a cassette recording of the BBC World Service interview I had taken part in. It was the morning, in fact, when I was off to Amsterdam for a short Spring break with the Hackney HIV/AIDS support group. As I was walking down the last flight of stairs I saw the postman push a small packet through the letter-box. I quickly tore it open and on seeing a BBC compliments slip wrapped around a cassette, decided to take it with me. I had no intention of going back upstairs with it since I'd locked up, and didn't want to leave it in the hallway until I returned.

On the group minibus to Heathrow, I noticed that the person in front of me had a Walkman on top of his holdall, so I asked if he would mind lending it to me for a little while. I prepared to play it with a certain amount of eagerness, having missed the actual broadcast. I was stunned by what I heard. What made it so powerful was that you could *feel* the emotion in my voice. And I was so totally engrossed by it all as I listened. I was unaware of anything outside.

"What is it you're listening to?" enquired the owner of the Walkman, who was probably intrigued at having seen me rewind and playback. "Oh, just something taped off the radio," I replied in a deliberately vague way, in an effort to discourage any further questions, since I had no wish to share the contents of the tape with anyone at that time. After three listens I had heard enough. In fact I was not to play it again for another sixteen months.

EIGHT

✣

Up, Up and Away with the Lift Appeal

Unlike the patient care at Mildmay, the lift was a bit of a joke. Using it, though, was hardly a laughing matter.

Having encountered problems with it when I was receiving care at Mildmay, the limits of my endurance were not to be reached until much later – just after I had started to run Mildmay's self-help office, in fact. I saw a patient in a wheelchair struggle, unsuccessfully, to open the heavy sliding gate even a single inch. Eventually, he had to ask me to help him in. It was a sad spectacle and it had the effect of making my mind up there and then. The solution seemed straightforward. The place simply had to have a new lift. A replacement was not considered a priority by Mildmay in view of a series of other developments in patient care. So it was down to me.

The task of starting it up seemed enormous. I couldn't do it all on my own; I needed some help. I mentioned it in passing to a few people, who expressed interest, but that's all. They weren't willing to *act* on their interest. I felt as though I was fighting a lonely battle.

After mulling over all the implications of taking on such a major project – the effort I'd have to make, the time I'd have to give and the overall commitment it would mean – I still decided to go ahead with it. How, when and where – in other words, the actual details – would have to be worked out later. I was eager to get on with it and, considering the urgency of the need, I derived little pleasure from employing any unnecessary delaying tactics, huge though the obstacles of undertaking it single-handedly appeared. *Mañana* never comes, as they say.

As it happened, fortune was on my side. Claire came round for dinner the next evening and we excitedly discussed the idea of taking on the Appeal together, independently of Mildmay and of anyone else. Everything then happened very quickly. The aims and the ideas flowed easily and it all seemed absolutely right for us to set on our course of action. Mildmay's chief executive gave us a *carte blanche* blessing.

The next morning, a patient's mother gave us our first donation of £100 towards the new lift and that was before we had even launched the Appeal. That settled it. Our vision had been reinforced in the most practical of ways. It was the best possible omen.

High on expectation, Claire and I happily created a fundraising strategy in the space of several evenings. We decided to concentrate on a small number of organizations (mainly pubs) and events (mainly one-off activities) which we hoped would yield a high return on our time and effort and raise at least three-quarters of the £35,000 target we were aiming at. We planned to get the remainder as a series of much smaller donations from a variety of individuals.

We wanted to *enjoy* raising the money, not find it an overloaded burden. We would be working on this in our spare time, both midweek evenings and at weekends, so it was crucial not to view the project as hard labour (in my case) or as an extension of work (in Claire's case). Our timescale of eighteen months incorporated a large degree of flexibility so as to allow for any periods of ill health or low energy. The campaign was very much a joint one, although I took much relief from knowing that Claire would still be there if I had to withdraw from any event for any reason.

Having sorted out all these details, we now had to let people know about it! I started telephoning various organizations to gauge interest and to gain support, and we designed a suitable flyer (and a poster version of it).

We kept it lighthearted in tone on the front, headlining it *Up, up and away with the Lift Appeal* and using the cartoon of someone in a balloon celebrating his getting off the ground. In the text we declared that you needed the biceps of a Schwarzenegger and the legs of Red Rum to muscle your way in. On the back of the leaflet we adopted a more serious tone, with some background information on Mildmay. We also created a Certificate of Thanks, which we would frame for fundraising organizations to display as a visual reminder of our appreciation. This would also serve as an additional form of publicity.

The Appeal swiftly gained momentum. Having a drink in a pub one evening, I got talking to the manager and persuaded her to agree to a benefit night specifically

to raise money for the Lift Appeal. The first benefit
– unlike the new lift – was now off the ground. Jungr
and Parker, at that time the support band for Julian
Clary's TV show, and well known on the pub circuit,
generously played for free. The Appeal was swollen
by £250 raised from bucket rattling and a raffle.

Word got round. Some people started to ring in and
offer to organize a benefit at their pub or workplace.
However, most of the time the approaches were made
by us to carefully selected people. No one refused point
blank, although let's say that some had to be worked
on a little more charmingly than others.

Attending all the fundraising benefits had the
additional advantage of being able to socialize for a good
cause. It was a night out for us each time! Give us a
promise of money and we'd be there! Of course, all this
was happening in our spare time and so we were
determined to enjoy the lighter side, once the
seriousness of our official representation was over. Even
so, it was not unusual to have to put aside the whole
evening and at least half of a Saturday and/or Sunday
in order to plan each event and then attend it. No
sooner was one event over than we had begun planning
the next one.

I was like a child with a new toy in terms of the
excitement and adrenalin I was experiencing. Every
time money came in, I used to get a real buzz out of
it. I felt I was doing something really worthwhile.
Claire kept detailed accounts of the Appeal income and
I delighted in seeing the running total for the lift
climbing ever nearer its target – large donations, small
donations, they all counted.

"How's it going?" people would often ask, aware of the existence of the Appeal, but not of all the details. I always think it's a good sign when people start getting nosy. The news of our project continued to spread. I used to visit the Units regularly and chat to the patients, during which time I would invariably mention the Lift Appeal as an item of interest. The replacement of a cranky old lift, which they found prohibitively difficult to use, was an issue they could all identify with.

In addition to one-off pub benefits and bottles of coins on their counters, funds were also raised by small organizations adopting us as their charity for the year, by one-off individual donations, gifts from churches and companies, small auctions and sporting events sponsorship – ranging from London Marathon running to parachute jumping.

But with barely two months elapsed, there was obviously still a long way to go to achieve the £35,000 target.

NINE

That Sinking Feeling

The agency that funded my self-help office at Mildmay had started to experience some major financial problems. Following several weeks of speculation, I received official confirmation that the organization was going into liquidation and was on the verge of closing down. As a consequence, the external funding for my post would dry up soon. (Although I received no salary for my labours – and it really was hard work at times on the emotional front – at least I could claim an allowance for travelling and subsistence.)

So that was that. Initially I was terribly disappointed, but on reflection and after having spoken to Mildmay's chief executive and medical director, who said that there would always be a place for me at Mildmay, I felt reassured and was determined to continue helping patients on a voluntary basis.

Aware of the situation, the Hackney HIV/AIDS support group approached me with the suggestion that they take control of the office and invite me to run it. This seemed a good idea at first since many Hackney residents came to Mildmay for care. However, with funding only available for people from this particular area, it would have meant not being able to help those patients from other boroughs. Since I wanted to extend the help to *everyone* coming in − from the whole of the United Kingdom and sometimes abroad − there was only one reply I could give. The invitation was politely declined.

Although I still carried on some of the work, without a base of my own it was rather difficult. My commitment, not surprisingly, dwindled. Furthermore, contact with patients on the Units was becoming too painful an experience. The deaths of two patients I had known quite well affected me badly. It was like seeing a mirror image of my own situation, except it was hazy − somewhere in the future.

However, I wasn't given the opportunity to wallow in the misery of it all, because the forthcoming weekend had already been mapped out for me. I had an early night on the Friday, since there was a long drive ahead of me the next day. The Welsh countryside beckoned! I was going to spend a few days with a group of friends who were already out there. It was wonderfully simple: the arrangements had been made some time before and all I had to do was turn up!

So off I headed for north Wales. It was a first for me: I had never set foot in the Land of Song before. The month of May was perhaps not an ideal time to go, but at least it would not be crowded with tourists and, receiving a free invitation, I could hardly complain!

I was going to a town called Dolgellau, in the heart of Snowdonia National Park. It is an area of outstanding natural beauty − the coast to the west, and mountains and woods to the north, south and east. Some old cottages had been rented to us for a remarkably low rate and, to my delight, they were heated by blazing log fires. As I sat by the hearth toasting bread on one of those antiquated long-handled forks, the pleasanter childhood memories rolled effortlessly back. I wondered why things also seemed to taste so much better when toasted on an open fire.

The clean fresh mountain air smelt ambrosial compared to the increasingly noxious surroundings of London, tainted by car exhaust fumes. I had looked forward to some long walks and gentle climbs. The view from the top of Cader Idris at almost 3000 feet was apparently exceptional, but not something I was willing to attempt. I kept to the lesser hills and still marvelled at the panoramic views I stumbled across. The weather was not perfect, but I was well protected against the cold and the damp, and for once it didn't spoil the sheer joy of the local scenery.

In addition to all this fresh air exercise, I took the opportunity to travel farther afield in my car. On the Wednesday I went off on my own, driving through all the old villages nearby and stopping off in a quaint little fishing village off the Barmouth Bay. It boasted an unusually large number of antique and second-hand shops and I was happy to browse around all of them. I bought some postcards and sat down to write them on the village green, soaking up a rare and short appearance of the midday sun. I then wandered back to the harbour front and bought some cod and chips, well seasoned with salt and vinegar and wrapped up in newspaper the way they used to be. I savoured every mouthful as I sat on the sea wall watching the harbour's boats and other small fishing craft gently bobbing up and down on the water. It harkened back to my younger days, but for once the trip down memory lane was not a painful one. On the contrary, it felt very reassuring to be repeating it all these years later, despite my prevailing solitude. I suppose it was all part of being on my own. And at times like this I did enjoy my own company.

I left it until the last possible minute to return to Dolgellau, but I knew that steaks and fire-baked jacket potatoes would be awaiting me for dinner. It would also be the last evening meal I shared with my friends before leaving the next day, so I felt it my duty not to be late and risk seeing everything burnt to a cinder. The next day, on the way home to London, I decided to split the journey and stopped off to visit my friend Peter in Birmingham. The walking, climbing and exploring had tired me more than I realized. I was able to benefit from a good night's rest and felt refreshed to tackle the next stage home in the morning.

I finally arrived back in London on Friday evening. I pulled up outside my home and walked through the front garden to find the iron security gate, which was normally always locked shut, swinging open. A little concerned, I ran up the stairs and came face to face with my own front door. Breathless, I just stood there looking up and down, registering my disbelief. A new frame had been secured to the door. I feared the worst. I nervously went inside and slowly started up the second flight of stairs. Half-way up my portable TV was precariously balanced on the edge of a step. The burglars had obviously been disturbed.

I immediately regretted that I'd been away. The log

fires, the beautiful scenery, the fish and chips by the harbour, the postcard writing on the village green, all these suddenly lost their charm. I felt that if I had stayed at home this wouldn't have happened.

The full details of the burglary did not emerge until much later. Although it was glaringly obvious by the empty spaces that electrical equipment had been stolen, there were smaller, more sentimental items plundered, too. My plants had been destroyed and soil rubbed into the carpet in a greedy act of violation. I was close to tears. I wasn't insured. I hadn't been able to afford the premium at the time and then it had just got left. Now it was too late.

It all felt very unjust; I shouldn't even have still been living there, for I had applied to my housing association to be moved several months ago. I had no option but to embark on a huge cleaning up process. It seemed that my drawers, cupboards, *everything* had been systematically searched. Floors, carpets, walls, woodwork, furniture, and several machine loads of clothes had all come in for the full treatment. As for the missing items, there was virtually no hope whatsoever in being able to recover them. They were gone. Forever.

The financial repercussions were extremely depressing. Faced with the prospect of trying to replace the essential things that were missing, I also had to continue paying rental on my main television which had been stolen – in other words, paying for something I no longer had the benefit of. Payment had to continue until a sufficient amount had been received to cover the loss of the television.

These events took their toll on me. I felt terribly

bitter and resentful over what had happened. Overwhelming tiredness developed into severe lethargy, after having expended so much energy into trying to make good of my situation.

I felt I had been desperately unlucky to have suffered a burglary in such circumstances. I had found out later to my absolute dismay that one of the tenants had carelessly left open the front gate *and* left the front door to the building on the latch, which meant easy access for opportunistic burglars. The police had been notified by another tenant who saw the damage to my own door and they had come round to investigate. On their authority a carpenter had subsequently effected a temporary repair to my door. Everything else in my flat, however, was as the thieves had left it.

The lethargy dug deeper into me. The burglary had made me feel very insecure. I gave myself mental torture over what personal information the people responsible had found out about me. I thought I might be at risk again if the burglars knew I had AIDS. The emotional effects were physically debilitating, often frightening. I would start feeling so dizzy and disorientated with exhaustion that unless I sat down immediately I would just collapse onto the floor. The thirty-something steps I had to climb – often several times a day were now for me like scaling Everest. On the good days, I was still able to go up one foot in front of the other. On the bad I was reduced to a slow crawl on all fours. I felt as though I had aged by a couple of generations. I wondered when my new flat would come through from the housing association because I couldn't face this much longer.

I continued to reflect for some time on all my troubles which had been exacerbated by the burglary and on the false promises from my housing association that I would be moved out. I already knew that a flat had been earmarked for me in a purpose-built block under construction. However, the building works had fallen behind schedule. I telephoned the housing officer for the latest update, knowing that if I didn't take the initiative no one at his end would. I was informed that it would be at least another three weeks before I could move — providing, of course, the flat was suitable.

By the time the weekend arrived I felt I just had to get away from my immediate environment, so I arranged to visit a friend's mother in Sussex. When Joyce had last been in touch with me, I had sensed a feeling of loneliness on her part. This was unlike her since she could generally always be relied on for a laugh and a giggle. I could only surmise that she had been missing Barry, her son, who had been in Australia since the beginning of the year.

It was a pleasure to see Joyce again and in such beautiful surroundings. She had a lovely little place in the countryside, a million miles removed from the metropolis I had just left and only a short drive from the south coast. We spent part of the afternoon walking along a deserted beach, invigorated by the cold sea breeze on our faces which blew away all the cobwebs from our mind. Soon enough, the subject of the conversation got round to Barry.

Barry was actually one of my closest friends and in times of hardship had always been supportive and available to lend a hand. But now he was in Australia for an indefinite period and I didn't know when we'd be able to meet again. His mother was worried about him being so far away and just wanted to talk things over with me. I actually felt quite envious of him out there, soaking up the sun when it had been so cold and wintry here. We both wondered how he was doing. Of course, he wrote from time to time, but there was never enough real detail to form a full picture. We found ourselves reflecting on the circumstances which had led him to his new, albeit temporary, country of residence.

He used to have a high-powered job in the City of London, but his company had fallen on bad times and, soon after celebrating his fortieth birthday, he found himself made redundant. He decided to capitalize on this unexpected opportunity by taking time off to travel. So he had set off for the other side of the world and had liked it so much he stayed there. I looked forward to the day when he would return so I could hear the details of all his escapades, doubtless over a few pints somewhere.

The weekend proved uplifting for both Joyce and me. I returned to London suitably refreshed.

Summer was coming, and I received a further boost to my morale with the news that *The Universe* was keen to extend its coverage of the AIDS issue. This followed the discussion of some interesting proposals with Claire on the possibility of making the focus a more personal one, by describing the everyday real life problems of someone living with AIDS – material for which Mildmay's work could provide an appropriate backdrop. It resulted in Ann Knowles, the editor, inviting us up to Manchester for the day to explore the opportunities with her. Subsequent to the AIDS feature her newspaper ran in April, I knew that the response generated by readers had demonstrated an intensity of interest which was not currently being satisfied. There was therefore an opportunity for *The Universe* to capitalize on this. In her office and in an excellent Italian restaurant over lunch we discussed the possibilities with her and Paul Burnell, the original reporter on the AIDS feature who had since become her news editor. In typical leader fashion for someone heading a newspaper which had a track record for breaking new ground, she gave her considered decision without any trace of wavering or uncertainty.

In addition to showing a further commitment to covering the AIDS issue – which was good news for Mildmay – she offered me the opportunity to tell my own story as part of a regular update. In other words, I could have my own column in the newspaper. I was asked to produce something in the region of 500 words approximately every three months for publication, to which I responded very enthusiastically.

Two weeks later I received some more good news, which I had eagerly been waiting for. At last an invitation came through for me to visit the new ground floor flat that my housing association had allocated me. Hooray! I was formally offered the accommodation, and I lost little time in accepting it. Granted, the site may not have been finished, the floors were bare and the rooms empty, with the exception of fitted units in the kitchen and appliances in the bathroom, but I could see there was potential. It was smaller than my previous flat, but I felt that the benefits (ground floor level, central heating, quiet location, parking space directly outside, amongst others) far outweighed its disadvantage of size. I even had my own small patio at the rear, which I planned to fill with plants, shrubs, trelliswork, and trailing ivy, or even roses. I closed my eyes and started imagining how the square patch of flagstones, bordered by sand-coloured walls, could be transformed in this way. I felt very excited by it all. Things were looking up!

First of all, though, I had to organize the actual move. I never realized how much of an ordeal it would be, how much of my strength it would sap. Years ago I would have taken it in my stride. However, a lot of water had passed under the bridge since then and my energy level was hardly at a peak. I had also accumulated a lot more equipment and furniture since those days.

So it was action stations. Now I had a real sense of purpose. I organized for the gas, electricity and telephone line to be connected in my new flat − and gave advance notice of my move to all relevant parties. Top of the list were my contents insurers. Soon after the burglary I had signed up my contents with The Salvation Army General Insurance Corporation, a non-profit organization, which meant premiums were kept competitively low.

I then went round the local supermarkets collecting empty cardboard boxes and started saving all my newspapers to assist in the process of packing which I did gradually, in the space of a week. A volunteer driver from the Terrence Higgins Trust kindly donated his time and his van for one of the several journeys that had to be made. The rest I made in my own car, with the help of friends. I lost count of the number of times I had to go up and down those flights of stairs, but the adrenalin was flowing and the whole event was overtaken by my excitement at moving to a new home.

Not that the removal went without a hitch. My solid oak dining table was too large to fit into my new flat, so I had arranged to sell it, to fund the cost of a smaller replacement. Its journey downstairs proved more difficult than I had imagined, owing to its sheer weight and size, even though I had a neighbour to help me. It slipped from my grasp and fell awkwardly down the last flight of stairs, smashing two of the legs beyond repair and damaging the top. The table around which many a memorable meal and important decision had been taken ended up in the dustbin.

The day after the removal, the physical effects hit me hard. The situation had reversed: tiredness had overwhelmed my excitement. It felt as though my arms and my legs were begging me to give in and go back to bed, back to the comforting warmth of my duvet, back to an indefinite lie-in. But that would have been too easy a submission. I didn't want to be out for the count. There was work to be done!

But though my mind was advancing in fifth gear, my body was in reverse. Nonetheless I made a start on cleaning up the flat. Thick dust from the building site seemed to have settled on every surface and in every corner. Only after I'd applied liberal amounts of cleaner and disinfectant could I think about finding a home for all the contents of the boxes.

There I was in a new ground-floor flat, seemingly happy with my lot. I was confident that this fresh new environment would lend me the new lease of life and peace of mind I so desperately needed. While I did not particularly like the immediate area in which I was situated, I could not deny its location was extremely handy. There was a newsagent, a late-night food store, and a greengrocer's just around the corner, a main shopping street 10 minutes' walk away; and a tube station down both ends of the road.

A week of frenzied activity followed, involving the arrival and assembly of some new furniture, the fixing of rails and hanging of curtains. Things were settling down nicely. My flat was becoming more homely by the day. All this provided excellent material for my first column in *The Universe* published in the 18 August issue, but, in truth, it was exhausting me! I was achieving progressively less as the week went by. I needed to relax, refresh, unwind. I needed to get away. So did Claire. Any idea of going on holiday had been postponed until I had moved into my flat and settled down, and it had taken longer than I had anticipated. We booked a late availability holiday to Ibiza for a fortnight in September, just sixteen days away.

The weekend before the holiday I had agreed to make a visit up north with a friend who was collecting a new car from his parents, the idea being to share the driving on the return part of the journey. The trip was uneventful until the moment we arrived back. Something was terribly wrong: there was an ominous empty space in front of his flat. My car, which I had left parked directly outside, was nowhere in sight.

Hurrying inside the block of flats, it was soon established that my friend's place had been burgled.

A great deal of equipment had been stolen, along with my car keys and house keys, which I had innocently left on the coffee table. The thieves had had no problems in matching the keys with my car and off they'd gone, probably using the back seat and boot for their loot.

And then I remembered. In the car I had left a private letter which carried my name and address. I hadn't a moment to lose. With my house keys in their possession, I realized they might have already paid my flat a visit. I rushed across London in a taxi, dreading what I would find, convincing myself I had already been cleared out. Stealing my car was bad enough; but in the boot, still in their carrier bags, were some new clothes I'd bought for my holiday the morning before. That upset me even more. I didn't have unlimited funds and couldn't afford to go out and replace them.

The door to my flat was securely shut. It looked as though the lights I'd left on were still on and the lights I'd left off were still off. Even so, it was agony waiting by my front door while the emergency locksmith gained access for me. My breathing was frighteningly irregular, but a sense of calm was restored when I realized everything was as it should be. No one had been inside. The locksmith stayed on to change the locks on the door as a safety measure, just in case the thieves decided to chance their luck. I had to hand over £100 for the privilege. It was £100 less to spend on holiday.

I had a phone call on the Sunday morning from the police to say that my car had been found and was secure. I expressed little surprise over this last detail, reminding the police that it would have been locked by the thieves themselves, who stole it, along with the keys, in the burglary. While not wishing to give the impression to the police that I was teaching them their own job, my eager impatience to be reunited with my car resulted in my recommending that it should be immobilized. This seemed an important step to take since for some reason I was told that it would not be possible for me to come and reclaim my car until the following day. Also, in compliance with security regulations, they could not tell me its exact location over the telephone; this had to be given to me in person at the police station.

Having had a spare key cut beforehand, I travelled down to the police station on Monday. I was shown on the map of the local area where the car was situated and immediately set off in high spirits.

I arrived at the road in question and after a cursory look up and down saw nothing remotely resembling my car. Never mind, I thought, it's bound to be round the corner. Again I glanced up and down the line of cars hugging both sides of the road and failed to see the one I was looking for.

I walked to the end of the road, carrying out a more detailed survey this time. I was willing each vehicle to change colour, shape, make, model, size. But it was to no avail. I checked the side roads, just in case there had been some mistake and then returned to the original road, hoping the situation had changed in my favour and I would see my car suddenly emerge by magic. But the absence of my car was not a figment of my imagination, just a cold, unwelcome fact. So I went back to the police station, staggered at the turn of events, to report it stolen again. Astonishingly I was met with little sympathy over this, though it was hardly my fault! In effect I was having to deal with the theft of my car twice over and come to terms with falsely raised hopes in between. I felt as deflated as last year's Christmas balloons.

The theft was relogged on to the computer and I was sent home, where I sank into a hot bath to help ease away my tiredness. I started mulling over the sequence of events. The attitude of the police left a lot to be desired. I would have expected them to have handled the situation a great deal more efficiently. They had my car in their grasp and seemingly just let it go. The car could have been anywhere by now. Maybe when it had been spotted, the driver was just stopping off at a friend's – who knows, perhaps a fence with whom to offload the stolen goods.

I also pondered over the possibility that whoever it was who had stolen the car might return there later on in the evening. As I lay in the bath, an idea sprang to mind. I could have indulged in some private detective work, going down to the area late in the evening to check the locality and then, if there were still no sign of it, to return there on the first tube of the morning. If the thieves were residing in that area, there would be the maximum opportunity to be reunited with the car before they had even woken up. I could have driven off, leaving them none the wiser.

In my emotional turmoil, I found I was searching the streets wherever I went, looking for any car that resembled mine and hoping it would bear my registration number. It was like looking for the proverbial needle in the haystack. Still, you live in hope.

I had been assured by the police that they would contact me as soon as they had any further news. I just hoped and prayed that somehow, somewhere, my car would get stopped.

I had to carry the burden of all this uncertainty with me on holiday. It was bad timing, but I had to try and make the best of it. Half of me just wanted to escape from the ordeal of it all; half of me wanted to stay behind in case there was news about my car. I also hadn't dismissed the possibility that an attempt might still be made by the thieves to enter my flat, even though my locks had been changed.

But then I reflected on how much I had been looking forward to going away and how this holiday had been postponed because of my moving home. The temperatures out in the Balearics would be in the high eighties and early nineties – that was an incentive in itself. Two days before the departure date I started up the motion of packing, sorting out which clothes to take and going out to buy some additional toiletries I needed. Finally, and most significantly, I bought my travellers cheques and a supply of pesetas. Ibiza here I come!

TEN

The Princess of Wales
and Broadcast News

It was in Ibiza, over a tuna sandwich and a glass of Chablis, that she popped the question. The curve of my mouth and glisten in my eye gave her my unequivocal response. The sun shone brighter. We felt like celebrating. Chablis tastes even better the second bottle around.

I can't remember how the subject arose, but I had just been invited to meet the Princess of Wales, and I was overjoyed at the opportunity. She was due to visit Mildmay in November, and Claire needed to ensure she had someone willing and available to fulfil the presentation role. It had to be someone who had previous experience in "going public", someone who felt confident and comfortable in front of cameras, lights and reporters, since this would be of major press interest. I decided I would worry about the details at a later date.

Afresh with motivation, we went on to discuss some fundraising ideas for the Lift Appeal. We wanted to do something unusual ... preferably abroad ... something to capture our own imagination and that of our potential sponsors. It was in my already elated state that I came up with the idea of going round photographing gendarmes in Paris. It appealed to our sense of fun and, because of its location, would probably entice more people to make pledges, in addition to receiving some press coverage. We thought it would be a good idea to embark on it later on in the year so that I could preview it in conversation with the Princess.

Discussing our thoughts on the royal visit and the subsequent gendarme-spotting idea had formed a very pleasant interlude and given me something to look forward to. I had been finding it difficult to relax; the theft of my car was proving a greater strain than I could have imagined. Had it been found yet? Had the thieves been caught? Was it lying abandoned somewhere? Had it been wrecked? The questions churned over in my mind relentlessly. Reading in the English newspapers about the continued spate of joyriding back home made my situation worse. It was a shame I had to carry all this with me while in Ibiza. I knew the police were dealing with the crime and I tried to convince myself everything would turn out all right, but deep down I wasn't too hopeful of a successful outcome by the time I got back.

I should have been more optimistic. Waiting for me when I got home was a message that my car had been found and was safe in a police compound at Gatwick (where we had just travelled back from). I was invited to get in touch with the police station there at the earliest opportunity in order to receive further details. The worries, the stress, the pent-up anger which had weighed so oppressively on me soon evaporated. I felt free again. Soon I would have my beloved car, my means of independence back, or so I thought.

I picked up the phone and dialled the number I had been given. The officer who answered was well acquainted with my case and informed me that since my car was carrying false number plates, I would have to obtain a new set showing my correct registration before I could legally drive it back home. It would mean a minor but irritating delay.

Retrieving my car turned out to be a nightmare. Number plates in hand, I returned to Gatwick after the weekend, only to be told that the investigating officer was not on duty until the afternoon and, unfortunately, he was the only one who had the authority to release the vehicle. It was clear that no amount of negotiation on my part would have been successful in making them change their minds. I was disappointed, but decided that the collection of my car would be well worth the extra wait. I went back into the main airport complex to while away the time reading newspapers and chain-drinking cups of tea.

Two and a half hours later, at two o'clock precisely, I headed back to the police station. I was surprised when I went outside to find it raining so heavily and, dressed solely in a short sleeved shirt and cotton trousers, came in for a soaking. The investigating officer gave me a full account of how my car had been found as I stood there, wet and bedraggled, with the rain dripping off me, forming a little pool on the floor. The thieves had apparently tried to alter my tax disc to reflect the new registration of the false number plates. A commendably sharp-eyed policeman had noticed the defaced disc and became suspicious. This impressive observation led to an arrest and the impounding of my car.

The drive home was an unpleasant affair. The car which had served me so well, had been a pride and joy, had given me my independence, and had felt like a friend, now handled like a stranger. I wondered who had been using it and who else had been sitting in it, but perhaps it was better that I didn't know. Of course I was relieved in being back behind the steering wheel, but I was hardly overjoyed at the idea of my car having been sullied and abused. The car felt incredibly dirty. I thought I could have wiped it clean and erased the past psychologically by having it serviced and valeted, but it wasn't as simple as that. The bad thoughts and memories persisted.

The drenching I received at Gatwick acted as the trigger to something I had probably been spoiling for – I came down with the flu. My defences were low. I was extremely tired – not the sort of "panting for breath" tiredness, but the aching tiredness you feel when you've struggled home from the supermarket clutching several heavy bags in each hand.

I made a concerted effort to get more sleep. Sometimes, however, I was prevented from doing so. My doorbell rang early one morning while I was still in bed. I got up to answer it, bleary eyed, having quickly draped my dressing gown around me. I was presented with a large brown envelope which, significantly, bore the stamp of Buckingham Palace, and for which my signature was required.

The sender was the Duchess of York. The contents

of the envelope included a mounted version of the colour photograph I had forwarded to her some time earlier as a small memento. It was the one which showed us in conversation during her visit to Mildmay. It came signed, complete with a personal greeting. There was also a message of support. I was flattered that someone in her position should have gone out of her way to send a personal note to me and I appreciated the sentiment behind it.

One week before the Princess of Wales' visit, I had agreed to feature in a short documentary advertising the importance of buddying schemes for people with AIDS. It was being filmed by London Weekend Television's Community Unit for their programme *The Day*. I was taking part with my own buddy, Kevin, and we were to travel over to Bruges as a pre-Christmas treat, which meant a horrendously early start. I set my alarm for four o'clock. I needn't have bothered.

Terrible stomach pains and a skin irritation which flared up the evening before meant that I couldn't get any sleep and had to stay up all night. So it was off to a bad start, before we'd even begun.

The van, containing the crew, had arranged to collect me from my flat at the unearthly hour of five o'clock, ready for the first part of the journey to Dover and the subsequent ferry crossing which would provide some significant early shots in the film. I thought the cameras might get more than they bargained for as I leaned over the deck railings and looked out to sea in supposedly reflective mood, I felt so ill. But it all went smoothly, thank goodness.

Bruges was beautiful, but the enjoyment of being

there was spoiled by the need to film sequences in a specific way and to repeat certain shots, including the longest indigestion-inducing lunch I'd ever experienced. It was starting to prove a little tedious, which only increased my anguish over whether I would last out the experience or succumb to the fast encroaching slumber . . .

It turned out to be a nineteen-hour day, which would be edited down to a couple of minutes! I was wrecked, almost unconscious with exhaustion, and stumbled into bed the moment I was home.

Not surprisingly, I had a long lie-in the next day, but during the evening I started giving some serious thought to my part in the Princess of Wales's visit — just six days to go. I was so excited to have the opportunity of meeting someone who has such a high profile in the AIDS field and of being one of the few people living with the disease to be presented to her.

Her high profile, however, meant she attracted large amounts of publicity. I would need to be prepared for such coverage. I grew worried at the potential consequences of going public again. The echoes were familiar ones. I had gone through the same thought processes with the Duchess of York's visit to Mildmay. However, the sequence with the Princess of Wales would constitute the most significant moment yet for me. I felt honoured, privileged, but very nervous over the imagined repercussions. I seemed to be creating stomach aches at will.

I was actually looking forward more to meeting the Princess than to seeing my face on the television and in the papers. My fears of wide exposure were soothed somewhat by the revelation that Terry Waite was expected to be released from captivity the day before the visit. I was reminded of how quickly news can happen. As with the Gulf War developments before I was due to meet the Duchess of York, hard news like this — news almost the whole world had been waiting to hear for years — would always, rightly, take priority. Maybe there would be no TV crew left to cover the Princess's visit.

There was. So the visit would be appearing on the national news. I wondered how many of all the people I'd ever known in my life would see me on the screen. How far back in the past would people remember me and recognize me? Old school friends? Old work colleagues? How would they all react? Would my more distant relatives in Scotland — some of whom still did not know I had AIDS — see me? I was overwhelmed with anxiety and riddled with doubts as to whether I should go ahead with it all.

I still had doubts while sitting in the conservatory on the actual day waiting for the Princess to appear. Once I caught sight of her approaching down the corridor, though, my fears dissolved. Like ice in the sun, they just melted away. I no longer felt nervous and now happily looked forward to what was a very special occasion for me. I already knew that the Press were to be escorted away from the area two minutes after the arrival of the Princess in the conservatory. This would allow us the opportunity for a more private conversation afterwards. Reminding myself of this gave me additional relief.

The Press were now all set to capture her entrance,

but she had other ideas! "Don't worry, Michael, I'll be with you in a minute," she laughingly said, on making a short detour into the lounge. The framed photograph of her previous visit to Mildmay had captured her eye and she went to take a closer look at it. Two minutes later she walked into the conservatory. I stood up and presented her with the flowers I had been safekeeping. The yellow roses and white carnations, laced with gypsophilium, combined well with the Princess's royal blue suit and the arbour in the conservatory completed the perfect backdrop. The TV crew and the national, local and news agency reporters and photographers capitalized on their two minutes, while the Princess and I happily conversed.

Then suddenly, with the departure of the Press, there I was alone with the Princess of Wales. Even her private detective and equerry retreated, closing the doors behind them. I learnt later that this was not the standard procedure!

I was deeply touched to have such an honour bestowed on me. It enabled me to talk freely and at length with the Princess and share my concerns with her about the developing AIDS situation and how there needed to be a greater knowledge and understanding of the issues involved. On a lighter note, in response to her request, I expanded on the fundraising trip to Paris, telling her it involved being photographed with as many French policemen as possible in the space of three hours.

The Princess spoke as openly as I did and she impressed me with the warmth and genuineness of her expression. The inspirational support she had shown to people with AIDS, just on this visit alone, would go a long way in heightening people's awareness of the disease. It was truly heartwarming — therapy at its best.

When the Princess left to tour the rest of the Unit and visit patients, I joined up with Claire and the Press again, this time on the Day Centre lounge, to do the TV and newspaper interviews she had lined up. At one point I confided that after having come out openly as a person with AIDS I was now scared that someone would put a brick through my window. I immediately regretted having said it. I knew that most papers would latch on to this quote . . . it had a slightly sensationalist ring to it.

The visit seemed to be a very successful one. Mildmay as a whole greatly appreciated the time and commitment shown by the Princess in support of the AIDS issue and the level of her interest and compassion was widely applauded, especially by the patients. The Princess had even asked to be kept personally informed about all the new developments at Mildmay.

Half an hour later the first edition of the coverage of the visit was broadcast on the lunchtime news bulletin. I could hardly believe it. There it was in the headlines, one of the lead stories, a large still from the film of my presenting the flowers to the Princess in the background, behind the newsreader. There was no going back at this point. The story had been well-produced; it was sensitively written and beautifully filmed, with an overall accent on living. I was delighted with the way it had turned out. The version used for ITN's 5.40pm slot was even better, there having been more time available to include the best shots and a smoother edit.

Regional news programmes also carried the story, as did Sky satellite news and Cable News Network (CNN) across the United States. I had to wait a little longer to see the take-up in the written press.

Claire and I were off to Paris the next morning, although we couldn't resist a sneak preview in the national dailies on the tube journey to Heathrow. Sure enough, the "brick through the window" had been highlighted.

ELEVEN

An Arduous Advent

We arrived at Charles de Gaulle Airport late in the afternoon. It was a bleak, grey, autumnal day in Paris – rather depressing, in fact – but it didn't succeed in dampening our spirits. We were looking forward to our gendarme-framing expedition, chiefly for the benefit of the Lift Appeal of course, but also as a source of amusement for ourselves. However, the event was not due to take place for another four days and the intervening period had been planned to allow for some sightseeing and relaxation.

We decided to make the onward journey by overground train and then the Metro, but later wished we hadn't. I certainly hadn't bargained on having to negotiate so many flights of stairs, while carrying a heavy holdall, plus obligatory duty-free carrier bag. Haven't they heard of escalators?

Our hotel was located in the fashionable St Germain des Prés quarter, a short meander past a variety of boulangeries, pâtisseries, brasseries and parfumeries to the banks of the Seine to face the Louvre and surrounding area. However, I was rather tired and in need of a short rest before setting out on an exploration of the local area.

Mid-evening we decided to brave the unwelcoming

weather. Although it was cold and miserable outside, we were soon warmed up by lashings of real French onion soup, topped by huge, garlicky croutons – the contents of an even huger tureen served up as a first course in a charmingly quaint, unpretentious, rustic little restaurant tucked away on one of the side streets on the outskirts of the Latin Quarter. I'd probably never be able to find it again.

The next few days we spent walking around Paris, seeing some of the more famous sights – indulging in the inevitable photographs showing the Eiffel Tower and Notre-Dame in the background. We avoided the traffic around a very busy Place de la Concorde, at the foot of the Champs Elysées, and took a lazy stroll through the Jardin des Tuileries, which looked a little bare at this time of year, yet still maintained an air of bygone elegance. There was also time for shopping (mainly of the window kind) at a very festive Galeries Lafayette and neighbouring department store Printemps on Boulevard Haussmann, just around the corner from the imposing Opera House, enjoying more celebrity than ever on account of its legendary Phantom and the films and musicals that he inspired. We had to wrap up well against the cold winds, but this provided a perfect excuse to check out a variety of bars, where the coffees and brandies were uniformly excellent

This all formed a pleasant introduction to the main event, so to speak. Paris struck me as being very picturesque and I would have loved to have seen more. However, I could feel my strength ebbing away and each day I felt progressively weaker, as though I were about to go down with a severe dose of the flu, except that it never came.

The fundraising extravaganza was successful, although it could have been phenomenally successful, were it not for an unfortunate bureaucratic error in the Ministry of the French Interior. A month before we left England we had arranged for clearance with a Chief of Police there to ensure that our "framing of the gendarmes" would not get us arrested. However, on the morning of our exercise, the senior officer who was dealing with our event was called away on emergency duty to the airport, did not leave the vital cover note we needed as our *carte blanche* for photographing the gendarmes, and, furthermore, did not even brief his staff! No-one was willing to give the authority for us to go ahead. It was sickeningly frustrating.

We were consequently unable to capture on film the gendarmes we saw. Instead of being able to claim for about 150, we felt it appropriately honest, in the circumstances, to reduce this to 50, seeing as we had no proof. Annoying though this was, maybe it was for the best. I would have raced around even more eagerly had we been able to use the camera. Besides, my health was rapidly declining by this stage and I had no wish to suddenly collapse on the streets of Paris through sheer exhaustion.

While in Paris we had anticipated being able to fit in a visit to Lourdes, but there was no way my body could have coped with the ordeal of a fourteen-hour return train journey so we decided to postpone it until some time in the new year. We also decided to come home one day earlier, owing to the deterioration in my condition, and advised the airport as such the evening before. Depressingly, on the morning we left, we learnt of the death of Freddie Mercury. It was an acute blow and made me feel even worse.

On arrival at Charles de Gaulle there were unexpected problems in changing our return flight, despite assurances on the telephone earlier to the contrary. I was becoming sicker, and needed to see my doctor in London. The circumstances, although not the fact that I had AIDS, were explained and repeated on several occasions to the very unsympathetic, indifferent desk staff. Finally, after broken promises and an extended wait of almost four hours in uncomfortable seating, without being allowed the opportunity even to have lunch in the restaurant, we were allocated standby seats at the shortest possible notice on the mid-afternoon flight. I breathed a sigh of relief. I was getting worse by the hour and was anxious to be home. Our luggage was checked in and we were shown to a separate waiting area and informed that our names would be called out over the PA system if the seats were still available.

Our names *were* called out, apparently five minutes later, but we didn't hear them because we had been escorted to the wrong lounge. So we had to reapply for seats on the next plane . . . and faced an hour and a half's further wait.

I eventually arrived at Heathrow, somewhat worse for wear. Standing by the luggage carousel is not the most exhilarating experience at the best of times. When every other passenger on the flight has departed, suitcase in hand, and you're left to stare at an empty conveyor belt, you know instinctively that something has gone wrong!

It had. Our luggage was lost. Heathrow Airport was unable to trace the bags at first and then deduced they must still be in Paris. We were advised to travel home without them. Once they had been located, they would be sent on by courier – which they were, at about half past ten that evening.

I was horrified at what I saw. My suitcase had not merely been damaged, but rendered completely unusable. There was a huge rip stretching along the top panel, offering an escape route for items inside. My iron, cushioned by jumpers and towels and supposedly well-protected in the middle of the suitcase, had also been broken in what must have amounted to some extraordinary rough handling en route from Paris.

Glad to be back? What with my increasing tiredness, low energy, a sudden rash of skin problems, and a protracted insurance claim for the flight baggage losses and damage, I was sinking into depression. At least during the next week we received a full letter of apology for the shabby treatment by the airline staff in Paris, and also some compensation.

Of course catching the flu in my condition proved comparatively easy and in due course it was aggravated by a bad chest. I grew worried about developing pneumonia and the idea of opportunistic infections taking a hold of me. I had no resistance to fight it. My white blood cell count was very low.

Despite all this, it was of some importance to me to go ahead with my plans to hold a party at my flat on 1 December. This was not just to remember World

AIDS Day and celebrate my appearance on television over the weekend in *The Day* transmissions (four in all), but also to welcome back Barry, who was returning from Australia that morning.

The Day was well received. Considering that I had had no sleep the night before the filming, I thought I looked surprisingly well. They say the camera never lies, so I must have suddenly become a good actor, because by mid-morning I had felt completely washed out and had to force myself to continue. Shortly after the programmes were broadcast I received from London Weekend Television a copy of the whole sequence of filming as a personal memento, which was much appreciated.

The following week I was walking along Camden High Street and suddenly found myself being hissed at, for no apparent reason. I was completely taken aback. I wondered if it was because someone had recognized me from my recent television appearances, either in the coverage of the Princess of Wales's visit to Mildmay in which I had come out openly as a person with AIDS, or in *The Day* broadcasts.

I wondered if similar forms of abuse would now start to happen more frequently. The fear of recognition was very real. Did my neighbours know? Were they keeping quiet on purpose? Were they watching my movements from behind their curtains? Could I feel safe in my own home? For a while I felt as though I were being stared at, followed, talked about. I felt very conspicuous. Was I just imagining all this? Was my mind playing games? Why was I being tormented so? London is a big city and you can live your life fairly anonymously if you wish. I was beginning to feel as though the whole of London knew about me.

"We saw your ugly mug on the telly and couldn't resist getting in touch," joked a couple of old friends I'd long since lost contact with. They had seen the broadcast on the news and written to me care of Mildmay. It made me realize that not every form of recognition was necessarily a bad one.

Some days, however, I didn't leave my flat at all and deliberately saw no one. I lay on the sofa, huddled under my duvet, staring through my french windows at the building site outside and becoming increasingly agitated by the monotonous to-and-fro of the workmen, who would invariably stare into my lounge. How dare they! It was developing into a real source of stress. Here I was in my own home, feeling under the weather and without even the privacy I craved. I didn't want to sit in my lounge with the blinds down all day, but sometimes I felt I had to, to avoid the leering eyes and stretched necks of the passing builders. I was furious at being made to suffer additionally in this way.

Advent was now here and I was surrounded by all the hype of Christmas and the happiness it is meant to bring, yet I couldn't drum up any enthusiasm at all. Most of the activities in the lead-up to Christmas just passed me by. Either I wasn't interested or felt in no state to get involved. The bells did not ding dong merrily on high for me that Christmas, they just rang hollow. I wished I could have been more enthusiastic, but my physical and mental condition seemed to block any improvement.

One thing which had to be done, however, was the

collection of all the sponsorship money from the gendarme-spotting in Paris. Almost all our advance pledges of £1750 were received by the third week in December. These would have exceeded £2000 had a pub not lost its sponsorship forms soon after the actual event. And we would have gone out and solicited even more but for the essential planning and preparations we had both been engaged in for the Princess of Wales's visit to Mildmay.

Christmas Day finally arrived. In the morning I drove over to Claire's and we merrily opened our presents together, before enjoying a leisurely coffee – lunch was a movable feast. I spent the rest of the day with Barry and his mother. Christmas Day always seems to last forever and this was no exception. Despite my spirits having been temporarily raised, I could not deny there was pain lying close behind the veneer, just waiting to escape and spoil things again.

I decided to escape myself. The day after Boxing Day I left London to take up an invitation to spend a couple of days with my friend Stephen at his parents' home near Manchester. I'd known Stephen for a number of years. He was a part of my social life when I was fit and healthy pre-diagnosis and, post-diagnosis, he still remained a part of it. Our friendship often involved long telephone conversations in which we'd talk over difficult days. We'd usually end up laughing. He certainly enjoyed a joke. He also enjoyed company and would often catch you unawares. He's the kind of person who would turn up on my doorstep clutching a bottle of wine and ask if I fancied providing a meal to go with it.

The short stay at Stephen's was very relaxing. His mother catered to our every whim, then sent us packing two days later back to London, with sandwiches, of course!

I arrived back in my flat just in time to catch the national headlines about a so-called new discovery in the search for a cure for AIDS. The combination of AZT and Acyclovir was being heralded as a breakthrough.

AZT (an abbreviation of zidovudine, the generic name used by doctors) was the first drug to be licensed for use in treating HIV infection. Tests had begun back in 1985. The drug supposedly acts to inhibit growth of the AIDS virus (HIV) thereby slowing down the spread of HIV in the body. Acyclovir is, incidentally, prescribed for the treatment of another virus — herpes.

Friends started ringing me to ask if I'd heard the news. But I was left confused. I had been taking this same combination for several months. Did this mean I was now cured? I was eager to learn more of the details. Was this the miracle we were all hoping for?

I rang my doctor at the Westminster Hospital to see if I could be enlightened further, but neither he nor the other specialists had any additional information to disclose. I suddenly felt unsure about the sincerity of the whole revelation. If it were true, surely they would have known. It left me disillusioned. My spirits were dampened yet again. Doubts crept into my mind. Perhaps it was just a cruel publicity stunt, taking advantage of the time of year when millions of people would be watching. If so, it had falsely raised the hopes of many people like myself.

I came to the conclusion, difficult though it was, that life should carry on as normal (whatever that was meant to be) and I put to the back of my mind any idea of being cured, for the time being at any rate. Once again there seemed little to look forward to, my poor health and melancholic state of mind casting a huge cloud on the horizon. What a miserable New Year's present. Welcome to 1992!

TWELVE

Be Bold, Be Strong
for the Lord Your God Is with You

I was sitting in the back of a taxi, on my way to Westminster Hospital for one of my regular out-patient's visits. Normally I'd be chatting to the driver, but this particular day was somehow different.

For one thing, there was an unprecedented amount of traffic. It was stop, start, stop, start, the whole journey. It allowed me time to think, time to reflect. My mind started wandering back to the events of what was now the previous year. All the negative things came to the fore. I remembered the situation in my previous flat last summer — the stairs, the cold, the noise. And I recalled the evening I returned from Wales to find my home burgled. I couldn't have taken much more. I just had to leave and when the offer of a ground floor flat came through, I had viewed it straightaway, was impressed, and lost little time in accepting it.

Isn't the ordeal of moving home, though, one of the most stressful things you can do? I was lucky — though I had to do all the planning, I did have friends to help with the rest of it. I couldn't have coped without their support.

I was happy in my new flat, with my own front door – that was something I'd always wanted. Goodbye to the communal entry!

I knew my mind was flitting at random from one subject to another, but I offered no resistance. It was as if I had a huge space available which a variety of thoughts, feelings and expressions were competing to fill. I started remembering all those people I'd known who were no longer here. One of the most inspiring had been Steve. I met him through a mutual friend while I was living in Stoke Newington and soon became friends ourselves. He, too, was living with AIDS and set a remarkable example and inspiration to others affected by the disease. I would never forget the affect he had on me when we were first introduced. I found his presence almost daunting. He gave off this tremendous spirit which then seemed to encircle and envelop you. He was a practising Buddhist and achieved great strength from his faith, which shone through in all he did. It was something I often marvelled at; it's not the kind of strength available on prescription. He had a sort of inner peace and contentment; he was seemingly without a care in the world and his energy knew no bounds. We'd often go out and sometimes dance the night away, just as any normally healthy person might, yet this was in spite of his appearance. His body was smothered with Kaposi's sarcoma, and he was bald because of continuous chemotherapy treatment for his condition.

He got on with his life and calmly dismissed those very elements of his appearance which would have had others stay indoors and conceal from the rest of the world. Only occasionally, when he was feeling drained after a particularly difficult episode of treatment, did he shy behind his front door. I wish more people could have met him and received that same injection of inspirational hope. When the time came, I felt incredibly honoured to be invited to his funeral. It was, I suppose, a typical Buddhist ceremony, but it was totally alien to my experience. For those who weren't Buddhists, the service was explained step-by-step. When his body was taken away, I was surrounded by peace and felt a surge of warmth throughout me. Although everyone was crying, there was a happiness in their tears, as opposed to an empty sorrow, and this was very uplifting.

However, that was then. The sense of loss I now felt deepened the malaise I was sinking into. I wondered what my family thought of all I'd gone through and all I was doing. They knew very little, really. It wasn't always easy discussing the traumas I faced from week to week. The journey of life in my case was not an easy one.

The scaremongering over Christmas and the New Year about an AIDS cure had been extremely distressing. The item should never have been allowed to hit the news; the claims about the miracle combination of AZT and Acyclovir were based on a very small, almost insignificant, sample, and remained unsubstantiated over time. The false hope it had raised was nothing but a cruel joke to play, a wicked publicity stunt. I still had lots of questions, unanswered, about how and why this could have happened and if any good could eventually come out of it. Was it worth my staying on these two drugs just in case there is a greater benefit to be had than first expected?

I often used to look at myself in the mirror and wonder if the AZT was doing any good at all when I saw the flaky skin, rashes and blotchiness which flared up every now and then.

I always felt worse in the mornings. I needed a couple of hours after I'd got up to wake myself into shape and get rid of the tiredness that seemed etched on my face. Getting out of bed was, in fact, the first major test of the day! I knew that having too long a lie-in, once I'd already woken up, would often exhaust me further. It was worth being strict with myself over this. I was also strict about my medication, taking care not to miss any doses and trying to keep to regular times. The tablets I had been taking twice a day were now something of a mystery. There was plenty of unfinished business to sort out on this one.

But it wasn't only my mind tormenting me during this taxi ride. My mouth was doing a good job, too. I was suffering from an attack of thrush and it felt very sore. My gums were bleeding, too, and in response my hand was automatically being directed to the source of discomfort. It was like having a mouth full of nails.

Then my stomach started up. The stabbing pains intensified, as if to test the limits of my endurance. What else have I got to deal with? Oh yes, my head of course. Now that was throbbing. It felt as if someone was knocking away at the inside with a hammer, and the pain was echoing all around. The suffering seemed never-ending. Is this real or am I imagining it? Surely there can't be a God up there or he wouldn't inflict all this on me. What else do I have to go through? Is this a living death or a dying life? I'm obviously *paying* for something. It's retribution. But what for? I could feel the anger surge within me. But then Jesus suffered, really suffered, in dying on the Cross. It happened to the best of them.

The weather did nothing to help my situation either. I looked outside and saw what appeared to be a decidedly grey, overcast sky. I was then distracted by the sound of a young child crying on the edge of the pavement. What is that woman doing to him? Perhaps he'd tried to run across the road. Poor kid, I bet he's had a few slapped wrists in his time!

I arrived at the Westminster semi-delirious. It's a good job they've fitted automatic doors, I thought, otherwise I'd have walked straight through the glass. Going down the four flights of steps to the Genitourinary Department was like going down the staircase to hell. Never before had the journey struck me as being so dark, so dull, so unwelcoming and so stiflingly hot. Every step took me further down into the depths of the hospital. Maybe one day I'll never get back up them.

"Please tell Adrian I'm here. I don't feel I can wait too long out here today. I want to get back home quickly."

I was so confused and upset that, although the waiting room was full, I didn't actually see anyone occupying the seats. I was just full of my own thoughts, my own distractions. Why had I been inflicted with this disease? Why couldn't I be sitting in an office doing a nine-to-five job, instead of standing uncomfortably in a clinic waiting room? Why couldn't I take the tube or drive to work every morning like millions of others and stand in a sandwich queue at lunchtimes? I can't do that any more. I can no longer rush around like I once did. I have to have a lot of sleep, eat properly. I've had to change my whole life.

Surely no one else can be going through the same agonies as me? When my turn came, I repeated out loud the question I had asked myself only a moment before and the doctor assured me that I wasn't the only one to suffer like this. He did his best to calm me down, recognizing the anxious state I had arrived in.

"But it's quite common for people in your condition to feel like this, Michael."

So I'm not the only one then, I thought. I was slowly beginning to see the reality of it again.

"Let's have a look at your mouth. It's obviously causing you some distress." I opened wide, only to be met with the comforting reply, "Oh, that's not such a problem. Take these pills and in three or four days you'll be fine."

It was good to have Adrian as my doctor and I trusted him completely. After all, I'd been consulting him for long enough.

"What about this rash on my legs?" I asked.

"Put this cream on twice a day for the next week. That should clear it up."

So in quick succession, my immediate medical problems were swiftly resolved.

Yet I still came out of my appointment feeling miserable. The news on the AZT and Acyclovir front was less than favourable. Everyone was being advised, at worst, to ignore it, so that hopes were not raised; and, at best, to interpret it with a massive amount of caution. And I'd been issued with yet more pills. Soon you'd be able to pick me up and hear me rattle!

Back out on the street, I noticed that the traffic was its usual heavy flow for the time of day, unlike on that fateful occasion when I had been diagnosed as HIV positive and was rooted to this same spot for what seemed an infinity. I looked again at the wall which had propped me up in my agony and turmoil. It was a painful memory. But that was then. This is now.

The reliving of that most painful event in the past had somehow strengthened me. I had come full circle and this time I felt I was coming out on top again. So what if I had more medicine to take. My ailments were being treated. Soon these problems would disappear. And when the next ones flared up, I'd get those treated too.

I looked up at the sky. The sun *is* shining, I told myself. It's not dull and grey as I thought when I arrived. Quick! There's my bus. If I run up the street I'll just catch it. I was no longer sure whether the thoughts were my own, or being implanted by someone else. But they came at the stage when I didn't mind one bit. I felt empowered all of a sudden. I had no need to take a taxi back home, I was quite capable of negotiating life on the bus and the tube!

Four stops and I was home. I noticed how people around me seemed to look uncannily happy. Was it something to do with me? Whatever the reason, it certainly made me feel better. The journey back home was totally different, formed such a startling comparison to the one I'd had in the taxi getting to the clinic.

I opened the french windows in my flat to let the fresh air and sunshine in. My mood was becoming more buoyant by the minute. I started to do some cleaning. I discovered an energy which I didn't have before. First I'm down and then I'm up. Life is so unpredictable! Perhaps there is a God after all.

Even so, I'll have to be bold, I told myself. I'll need all the courage I can muster to continue fighting. And I'll have to be strong, 'cos this thing ain't getting me yet! I remembered my Auntie Anna, who lights a candle for me every day. Perhaps her faith, with the faith of others, is indirectly strengthening me. I'm in her thoughts when she says her prayers at night. And I know I feature frequently in the thoughts of certain friends whose faith is very strong. I know I'm not forgotten.

Since I started to do an occasional column in *The Universe*, I know that other people, besides my friends and relatives, have been praying for me too, although I am by no means in constant contact with them. My published diary extracts have produced a good response from the paper's readers. This means a lot to me.

I take comfort in knowing that the faith of other people, as well as my own, sustains me. My beliefs remain intact, though sometimes lie dormant, in limbo, unexpressed, unacknowledged, for long periods. My questioning over the existence of God always tends to happen in my darkest hours and, once out of them, I often despair at my temporary agnostic leanings. They generally arise from my disillusionment linked with my inability to always understand the pain and suffering attached to my AIDS condition.

Although I freely admit that I do not go to church or confession regularly, I am happy with what I believe and surely that is the best possible foundation.

THIRTEEN

Packing It All In

After the doubts, reassessment of my life and onset of medical problems leading into the New Year, I managed to drag myself up and start walking tall again. It had been one of the worst periods I'd known in terms of the erosion of both my physical reserves and of my positive thinking. Your health suffers further if you allow things to affect you seriously for any length of time.

After all the news stories about AZT, it was ironic that the drug should now be contraindicated for me. On my second visit to my doctor at the Westminster in the New Year, he expressed concern at my low blood count, which showed I had very few white cells in my body to fight off infection. He strongly suggested I stopped taking AZT, which he believed was making the situation worse, and transfer to another anti-retroviral drug — a newer alternative by the abbreviated name of ddi.

Dideoxyinosine, to give it its full name, was quite a mouthful in more ways than one. It came in the form of a white powder which you then had to mix with water and drink — preferably with a clothes peg on your nose. It both smelt and tasted absolutely foul! One of the disadvantages of ddi was that it had to be taken on an empty stomach, which sharpened the insufferable, lingering taste. It is apparently released slowly into the body, and because it contains an antacid powder, it is prevented from being destroyed by the acidity of the stomach. Another disadvantage was that the introduction of such a strong drug produced a severe shock to the system, and the body had to adapt. This could often be uncomfortable. It was not uncommon to suffer chronic diarrhoea during the first week of taking it.

The drug was still unlicensed for use and I was aware that trials to assess its effectiveness were in progress. However, I accepted my doctor's advice and decided to try it out for myself. Conscious of the side-effects, and in need of a period of complete rest as my body adapted to ddi, I referred myself to Mildmay's Elizabeth Unit for five days. (I was able to make a self-referral on account of already having been a patient there.) Friends came to see me, however, so that I had company at some time every day. The change of scenery was crucial to my physical and mental re-habilitation. (Shame the food hadn't improved much!)

An early highlight of 1992 came with the opportunity to meet the pop star SEAL. Claire invited me to join her in representing Mildmay at a benefit concert he was doing on 14 February to raise funds for Mildmay's planned Mother and Child AIDS Unit. The Valentine's Day concert was organised by Marie Helvin on behalf of AIDS Crisis Trust and took place at the Hammersmith Odeon, "London's premier music venue", as the publicity blurb for it goes.

It was excellent timing to have SEAL appearing in

a Mildmay benefit that week. The singer had just collected a string of awards from the music and entertainment industry. He was in peak demand.

Backstage passes allowed us the opportunity to meet a variety of people we wouldn't otherwise have seen, including, most importantly, the person who was instrumental in enabling the benefit to take place — Marie Helvin. She was very interested in Mildmay's work and was immediately updated with what was happening.

The concert itself showed SEAL at his exuberant best — an excellent live singer and performer, with the audience declaring its enthusiasm with no holds barred. Prior to SEAL's coming on stage, a guest appearance was made by Elton John, a Patron of AIDS Crisis Trust. He flew in from abroad specially for the occasion, to declare his support of SEAL and endorse the work of Mildmay in setting up its world first Mother and Child AIDS Unit. He was warmly applauded. I understand he then flew back to wherever it was he had come from!

After the concert and some drinks backstage, we continued on to a private party SEAL was holding in an American bar in Covent Garden. The party started around midnight, so it was a long day! It was here that Claire and I had a personal opportunity to thank SEAL for his generous support and expand on Mildmay's work. The occasion gave me the extra boost I so needed. It was, in fact, the perfect prelude to my fast approaching trip to Australia. Ten days later I would be on the way to Sydney via Minneapolis and a short stopover in Los Angeles.

I grew terribly worried about the effects on my condition that a 28-hour flight might produce. I even wondered if I would survive the journey, let alone the four-week holiday. If I weren't in good physical health at the time, the flights would exacerbate every defect and weakness and I would be in serious trouble. (If I were in less than satisfactory health I wouldn't be able to fly at all, on doctor's advice.) To make matters worse, I could not take my medication with me. If I had been found in possession of AZT, ddi or any other prescribed drugs for an AIDS condition, I would have been refused entry by United States immigration. The country had a policy of not allowing in any people known to have HIV.

I couldn't take the risk of being pulled in for questioning and then sent back to England. I would have preferred the ground to have swallowed me up there and then! Yet this was a big risk. However, I knew that as long as I made it without incident to Sydney I could obtain any drugs I needed at a general hospital there. It was a huge source of comfort knowing that my doctor and the other AIDS consultants in the team at the Westminster Hospital knew the Sydney doctors and would be able to arrange any request very easily.

I was on such a high, never having travelled to this part of the world before. Not many people from the other side of the globe have! I felt extremely privileged to have the opportunity. I'd not even been to the United States before, although the stay in Los Angeles was no more than a stopover.

I was flying to Australia with my friend Barry, who

used to live there, and who made this trip possible for me. He was good to have as a guide since he knew all the sights and sounds and favourite old haunts. (He also assured me that postcards sent *from* Australia to Great Britain would take considerably less than the three months it took the card I posted to him in the little Snowdonian village of Dolgellau. In the age of supersonic air travel I think that this one must have swum there on its own, via Antarctica perhaps.)

My only previous contact with Australian people had been via the naïve portrayal of life in TV soaps such as *Neighbours* and *Home and Away.* Could the simplicity of Ramsay Street really provide a snapshot view of Australia as a whole? Somehow, I doubted it. And sure enough, in reality, it was very different.

Sydney was surprisingly cosmopolitan, allowing a rich variety of cultures and lifestyles to flourish quite harmoniously. And I was deeply impressed with the warmth and friendliness of its people. Although the city had a vibrancy, an energy and a vitality all its own, it could be as relaxing as you wanted it to be. However, I couldn't resist doing the tourist bit and visiting, amongst others, the famous Opera House and Sydney Harbour Bridge. Not to have indulged in seeing these landmarks would have been unforgivable! And it was possible to eat out in good restaurants every night because it was so cheap to do so. It was a seafood eater's paradise, but then the meat, the salads and the white wines were just as special, too.

The superb sunshine permitted frequent excursions to the beach — wherever you are in Sydney you're never more than a few minutes away from one — and seemed to spark off a very positive effect in me. My skin problems virtually disappeared. I looked and felt healthy, almost to the point of actually forgetting I had AIDS. My inner self was very strong.

All good things have to come to an end and the return date in mid-March loomed ever nearer. Unfortunately I had to return to England alone, since Barry decided to stay in Australia for a little longer. The struggle home, made worse by my travelling without company, seemed to last for days. I was dismally bored during the journey and started experiencing some physical discomfort, caused, I learnt later, by the cumulative effects of an excess of sun on my condition. You can't have it all!

Ten days later I was due to travel to Lourdes with Claire. Thanks to the generosity of *The Universe* readers, I had managed through an appeal in my December column, to obtain the required number of Air Miles vouchers to cover the whole trip. But I didn't recover in time and, to make matters worse, I was developing bronchitis. My GP said there was absolutely no way I should fly in my condition. So there we had our answer. We had to postpone, for the second time.

Getting back into the old routine in my flat proved somewhat arduous at first. It's surprising how quickly you can adjust to a new lifestyle, especially on holiday. I had to work hard to motivate myself. I had met some lovely, friendly people on my travels in Australia. By sheer coincidence one of the first people I met there, Robert, happened to be making a trip to London in less than a fortnight's time to visit his twin brother.

While in London, he stayed at my flat for a while and the Australian theme continued.

But things soon turned sour. We had gone out for Sunday lunch, and coming home, I noticed that the front door had been boarded up − a sign that something sinister had happened. Standing right in front of the door, I could see that it had been kicked in.

With my heart rapidly sinking into my stomach and tears welling in my eyes, I nervously went inside. The place had been ransacked. In shock and despair I surveyed the damage: large empty spaces on the floor where my television, hi-fi and other equipment had stood. There were holes in the walls where my speakers had been ripped out of their brackets, leaving great chunks of plaster on the carpet. Drawers had been rifled. My private correspondence file had been opened. I had even suffered the loss of a sentimental old cigar box full of money I had religiously been saving to pay my telephone bill. The thief had also taken other money, jewellery, and Robert's camera.

It transpired that at some time after the burglary a passing neighbour had witnessed my door ajar, taken a quick look, and informed the police. The police had in turn arranged some temporary security measures and left a note to say that they had been inside my flat, with the request that I should contact them when I got home.

This second burglary reopened all the old wounds. History was repeating itself, making me relive the bad memories. I felt violated all over again. The loss of money put paid to the idea of visiting my brother, James, in Scotland the following week. There were just too many problems to sort out. I would not have felt happy leaving the flat.

If I had gone, though, at least my absence would have spared me the revolting spectacle three days later of dog excrement posted through my letterbox. Was this just a common criminal act, or was it fuelled by the fact that someone knew I had AIDS? Disgusted at such an outrageous incident, I got down on my hands and knees and cleared up the offending area without a moment's delay. Then I collapsed on the sofa, my head in my hands, and wondered where I went from here.

I was left with the task of rebuilding a home I had moved to less than a year ago. Its ground floor location was one of the features which had attracted me to it. Now it was shouting out to me its vulnerability.

I thanked God I was insured this time. At least it would soften the blow financially. I sent off a claim form backed up by a police report the next day, and within four days a cheque from the Salvation Army for the correct amount plopped through my front door. I cannot recommend them highly enough!

I was quite excited, on the one hand, to have the means to replace everything which had been stolen, but, on the other hand, I wasn't sure I liked the idea of buying new equipment to bring back to my flat only for someone to burgle again. Besides, perhaps someone was watching me in the flat, in which case they could have waited until they saw me go out, then nip in and strike again. How many knocks does a person have to take?

Not surprisingly, my health plummeted. I got the flu complete with swollen glands and night sweats. Out of sheer exhaustion I felt powerless to do anything. It was like waiting for the next chapter of the story to unfold. I was scared to go out for fear of what I'd perhaps come back to. My skin broke out in a rash, so then I didn't particularly want to go out anyway. I was imprisoned by four walls and painful memories.

My birthday was coming up and I was not getting any better. I had planned a party, inviting a small number of friends, but when I felt even worse on the actual day, I was obliged to cancel. My degenerating ill health, largely due to the stress of the burglary, had got the upper hand and spoiled things. Happy Birthday, Michael . . .

If only these people knew what they'd done to me. To me it was much more than just a burglary. My personal security – my sanity, even – was at stake. It wasn't just physical problems I had to cope with, but severe mental anguish. The walls of my resistance had come crashing down around me and left me vulnerable again.

The effect of a burglary on someone in my position can be almost catastrophic. I started considering the possibility of moving away from London. But in the next breath wondered why I should. Why *should* I feel obliged to up and leave a flat I really liked? I'd not even lived there a year. It would have been very unsettling, not to mention downright exhausting, to have moved to somewhere else. The upheaval of moving to this flat last year, following the previous burglary, was a memory which would remain crystal clear. I would not want a repeat performance of it.

The possibility of installing further security measures

seemed to be my best option. Since I didn't want to
be hounded out of my home, I needed to take action
to increase the safety in my present environment. I
decided to work out the details of what I needed at the
earliest possible opportunity, once I had recovered from
this latest bout of illness. All I knew was that I wanted
an alarm to be fixed to my flat. I had no desire to hide
behind bars, thank you very much. Friends arriving
at my flat would think they're coming to a prison. And
more and more I was of the opinion that to move would
have been giving in to the burglars. Who were they?
Where were they? What did they do (apart from
burgle)?

If only I could have got hold of them. Mind you,
it wouldn't have achieved very much. I might have been
putting myself in danger. You just don't know how
some of these people are going to react. I just hope they
have a conscience of some sort.

I switched the focus of my attention back to me,
while I lay on the sofa reflecting on all of this. I wasn't
getting enough sleep because I felt my flat – with me
in it – was at risk. It was as though I were being
watched. My nerves were on a knife's edge. I believed
that there could be someone just waiting out there in
the dark, ready to pounce once my lights had gone out.
So I left the lights on all night, which made it even
more difficult to drift off to sleep. But it seemed a safer
option.

For a long time I had deliberately avoided having
to replace the stolen goods. In my subconsciousness
I thought that the burglars might see me carry the
boxes of new equipment into my flat, and then smash

their way in to steal again. In an exaggerated sense of security I even considered the idea of covering up any new boxes of equipment with blankets – simply to disguise the nature of the contents. The lengths you have to go to in an effort to throw people off the scent! In retrospect I suppose this sounds highly amusing, but at the time I was deadly serious and believed such action was essential, because I was obsessed with the idea that I really was being watched.

I wondered where I should go from here. Once again I bemoaned the fact that I could no longer be an ordinary nine to fiver. It was really difficult at this time just to keep going every day and think of the remaining positive elements in my life, when so many bad things had been happening. I didn't just have to live with AIDS, I had to fight prejudice and the uneducated ignorance of society in general. I was having to live in fear.

Two hours later I was still lying on the sofa in the same position. It was the evening of my birthday, the time when friends should have been filling my flat. I noticed it was getting dark outside and decided to close my blinds fully and transfer to my bed to try and slumber off some of the worries and fatigue.

FOURTEEN

Who's Questioning Whom?

I often wonder what it must be like for my friends.

I try to put myself in their position and think how I would react to my illnesses, my ups and downs, my mood swings, my sudden tirednesses, my changes of mind. I have to admit that I would find it very difficult. Some of them deserve a medal. It must take someone very special not only to believe and accept the swings and roundabouts in my life, but also to understand, or be as close to understanding as is possible, when that someone does not personally have AIDS.

Imagine the scenario. Let's say I've arranged, a month in advance, to meet up with a friend in Cambridge – someone I haven't seen for ages. We planned to have a spot of lunch and then spend the afternoon walking round the city, admiring the colleges and looking at the shops. When the day arrives, I feel really rough – I wake up feeling as though I haven't slept for a week. Perhaps my gums are also sore, or my mouth is ulcerated, or my ear infection has chosen this particular morning to flare up again and I am generally experiencing discomfort way above what a normally healthy person's threshold of pain would be. Whatever the symptoms or the reasons, I am in no fit state to journey out of my flat, let alone London, then roam around the shops in and out of the cold; and I do not want to allow a friend the indignity of seeing me turn up when I am obviously much too fatigued and am suffering from some kind of infection. But will this friend believe me, accept what I say, understand the situation when I make the telephone call to cancel?

I dial the number. "Hi, it's Michael." At this stage I'm already feeling guilty and embarrassed, knowing that this person has arranged things around me. "I'm really sorry, but I'm afraid I won't be able to make it today. I'm not feeling too good."

Then follows the crunch moment, when I instinctively ascertain whether or not my story has been believed. I know that some friends occasionally think I'm laying it on, perhaps exaggerating my condition a little, just because (in their minds) I don't fancy spending time with them or simply making the effort.

Indicative of this is an awkward silence at their end — probably only for a couple of seconds, but nevertheless a silence that assures me that they do not believe me. Thus they give themselves away. Perhaps in the silence there is a hurt, even anger, which they are struggling to control and conceal before responding. This makes me feel even worse, as if I'm deliberately dampening a friend's enthusiasm, which, of course, is never my intention. Sometimes I even question myself as to whether I'm telling the truth or not, and I feel inwardly concerned at the possibility of making them feel rejected. Things can get complicated very quickly.

The usual response, however, I'm thankful to say, is an immediate one of concern: "Oh, Michael, what's

wrong?'' I then proceed to explain the situation, the
depth of detail depending on how close the friend is.

But even then, acceptance is not guaranteed. Some
try to cajole me into changing my mind. Others may
be a trifle blunt, on the pretext that I'm wallowing too
much in the proverbial misery and a change of scenery
will help me "snap out of it". Only rarely does this
persuasive approach work. A change of mind can lead
to a great deal of regret if my condition worsens when
I'm miles away from home and it's evident I shall have
to leave early. I then become angry at not having
listened to what my body was telling me in the first
place and transfer this anger to the friend who
persuaded me to come on out. Everyone ends up losing.

With those friends who accept my story, there are,
I feel, varying levels of understanding involved. I think
you need great strength of mind and a creative
imagination in order to attempt to understand the
everyday, the short-term, and the long-term problems
and implications of an AIDS condition on the human
being if you are only affected (and I do not intend to
be disparaging) as opposed to *in*fected. Deep down, few
people are able really to understand. You are naturally
drawn to the company of those who do. It creates a
special bond, without which the sense of loneliness and
isolation surrounding my condition would be one of
depression.

I confess I do sometimes call into question whether
I should show more willing when I cancel
arrangements, especially at short notice. I get no
enjoyment from making the actual cancellation and
agonize before, during and after the "dirty deed". But

I believe I simply have to play safe, and not take any risks when my health is at stake.

Sometimes all I fancy is an early night, rather than going out. If I urgently need some privacy and peace I'll resort to switching on the answer machine and monitoring the incoming calls. Being a temporary recluse is no bad thing if it helps ensure you'll be back on your feet by the morning.

The ability and the desire to understand is a precious gift. Thank you to all those friends who exercise it in such a positive way for me.

FIFTEEN

🦎

Lourdes – Alarmed and Uplifted

It may have been for the third time of asking, but my visit to Lourdes finally took place at the end of April. It was well worth the wait.

I mused that perhaps the two previous attempts had been foiled by divine intervention. On a more serious note, perhaps I actually *was* being told I shouldn't go. I would have got little out of it in view of my low energy level (in Paris) and my illness after my return from Australia.

During the week before the trip, I had seen a marked improvement both in my physical condition and in my psychological strength. The support of close friends had made me more resolute. Comforted, cheered and calmed, I determined to stop being defeatist – so unlike me, really – since it had been running me down.

My natural instinct has always been to get up and fight, not to give in. The only exception is when my positive attitude is no match for the times when my energy level drops so low that I feel I can do no more – just rest, recover and recharge myself, ready for the next personal battle.

The problems of the previous weeks had been put behind me. It seemed the time was right to go. I was very excited on the outward flight to Toulouse, where we would be staying for three days. However, things don't always run smoothly. About twenty minutes before our scheduled landing time, the captain announced over the PA system that for the last half an hour we had, in fact, been circling around. We had made a 360 degree turn and were on our way back to Heathrow! The captain explained that he was not happy with the performance of one of the engines and, as a precautionary measure, he had decided to return to have it checked, with the possibility of transferring to another plane.

I looked at Claire, who shared my worries that perhaps one of the engines had packed in. It had certainly produced a very strange sound on take-off, I had to admit. Although we decided to make light of it, we did actually wonder whether we would make it to Lourdes. I thought it might be a case of third time unlucky. Surely there wouldn't be any more setbacks to stop us getting there?

Thankfully, there weren't. We arrived several hours late, but safely, at a very attractive hotel we had booked about a month before. It produced an immediate calming influence, set in its own peaceful courtyard and surrounded by lush greenery. It was named after Jean Mermoz, whom I soon learnt from the hotel literature was "a pioneer of Europe's airborne exploration of the world, from Senegal to the heights of thē Andes"! Assorted photographs, paintings and illustrations of this man – a hero by all accounts – and his exploits tastefully adorned the Reception walls.

I had a short siesta soon afterwards to counteract the tiring effects of the trip. I have learned that I must listen to my body and respond with the appropriate action, otherwise I end up suffering much more. It is a simple formula, really. If I feel tired, I have to have a rest — a sleep, if I can manage it. Otherwise my tiredness will wreak havoc on my body and lead to further associated complaints.

We ate close to the hotel that evening. Lourdes was a two-hour train journey from Toulouse and we were making an early start the next morning. I knew we were close to our destination when I saw the imposing and beautiful mountains of the Mid-Pyrenees, in which Lourdes serenely nestles. It was my first visit to this area and it felt very welcoming.

Walking through the main gates to the real focus of Lourdes — the inner sanctum which houses the main church, basilica, Grotto, baths, etc — I experienced a lovely sensation of inner strength. On a more down-to-earth note I was impressed by the total lack of commercialism within the grounds. There were no vendors of any description whatsoever. The presence of tacky souvenirs here would, for me, have trivialized the very essence of Lourdes. In any case, the main street in the town through which we had just passed was teeming with gift shops, all selling the same variations on a theme.

The only things for sale in the grounds were candles of all sizes, for which the relevant donation was enlisted on trust. There wasn't even anyone to check whether you placed the correct amount — if, indeed any amount — in the wooden collection box. But would anyone be mean enough to want to take advantage of such a free and open system?

The Grotto was the first port of call. I was grateful for the large amounts of space in which to move around without restriction. It meant I could stand and stare at the hewn-out rock and the spring, which welled up, as the story goes, under the hands of Bernadette Soubirous way back in 1858. Thousands, millions maybe, have stood in the same place over the years. I wondered how many of them had AIDS. I also gazed at the statue of the Virgin Mary in the very spot she was seen to appear. I found myself reflecting on the extraordinary history and significance of this particular area and the reality of my own condition, and I hoped the visit would be of some lasting benefit. I was also thankful that there were no jostling crowds to desensitize the experience, just the occasional passer-by as to be almost peripheral. I never felt I had to move on from the spot to which I was rooted, was never made to feel I had outstayed my time allocation and ought to make way for others.

The subsequent bathing of my face with water from the holy spring seemed blessed with an additional significance. I filled a large empty Evian bottle with a further supply of water so that I could dab some on my skin for the mornings to come.

We then felt drawn to go into the main church, where we had the space and privacy to reflect, pray and absorb the very special atmosphere. Eyes glistened and tears were shed. It was all a very natural experience and very touching. The freedom to indulge in moving personal gestures such as these heightened the joy of being there. I was filled with an inner peace and warmth which to me was a very precious gift. I may not have received the cure I was perhaps deep down hoping for, but in the solitude I could hear a voice comforting: "You're not alone."

In raised spirits I suggested we took some pictures to record the occasion. Claire had previously photographed me in and around the Grotto, but we also wanted ones of us together with the beautiful hills of Lourdes as the backdrop, so we asked one of the few nearby tourists to oblige.

After walking through the grounds and soaking up the surroundings, finding amusement in the antics of some of Lourdes' more distant visitors and wincing at the sight of huge black antiquated hospital perambulators (complete with hood) – used for taking ill or infirm people around the grounds – it was time for a spot of lunch.

We chose a small place well off the tourist trail and spent a couple of hours there, remembering the events of the morning. Claire complained that the jug of red wine didn't seem to be emptying at all. Normally this would not constitute a complaint, but after what must have amounted to the tenth glass, I could see her point. Doubtless the jug would be served up to the next table, miraculously full, without the need for a top-up. Either that or the glasses were exceedingly small. I suspect it was the latter.

Lourdes had provided a memory which will stay with me forever – moving and inspiring, emotionally fulfilling and spiritually uplifting. It had been a challenge to the senses and yet also a haven of rest. After the inevitable coffee and brandy – a now all-too-familiar trademark – in a bar opposite the railway station, we kissed goodbye to Lourdes and snoozed our way back to Toulouse.

Not surprisingly on my return to London I felt somewhat deflated. The excitement of Lourdes stayed with me, but it was a case of having to carry on with my life where it left off. But at least I'd now been to Lourdes, something I'd wanted to do for a long time. And the longer I go on, the more hope I think there will be of finding a cure, in addition to establishing new ways of treating people with AIDS prophylactically. Maybe I'll have the strength to continue and be around for it.

In the meantime, the constant ups and downs in my life continued to do battle on a see-saw of intensity. For one period I might be feeling spiritually uplifted — as with Lourdes — but then, lo and behold, something would happen to upset the applecart. One bad apple keeps the doctor on call.

Since I so wanted to remain in my flat, I decided I had to make the best of it. I had my flat redecorated, not only to lend a fresh outlook, but also to cover up the visual reminders of the damage caused by the burglary and to breathe more of me back into it. The ugly holes created in the wall by the wrenching out of my hi-fi speakers was a source of stress each time I came into the lounge. They were in such a position and at such a height that I could not avoid seeing them, and knowing they were there seemed to attract my eyes even more, against my wishes.

Things seemed to be settling down again. Perhaps the worst was now over. Having created a new look in my flat, I went out to buy a hi-fi, television and video, all funded by my insurance claim. The empty spaces, which signalled such bad memories, were filled again. I even found time to hang an original painting Claire and I had acquired back in February, after a couple of visits to a Spanish wine bar in Highbury where it had formed part of an exhibition. The painting was an exquisite reproduction of *The Ignudus* (translated as *The Unknown*), a detail from Michelangelo's ceiling of the Vatican's Sistine Chapel, in which the classic features of the unknown man are shown reclining against a stone pillar.

After the brief excitement afforded by the hanging ceremony, it was back to sorting out the essentials. I still hadn't managed to fund the cost of an alarm to my flat and there were outstanding security measures to be addressed by my housing association. However, my sleep pattern was starting to improve. Much of my energy had been restored. I was starting to feel more at ease and at peace with myself.

And yet if I could have seen into the future at that point, I would not have liked what I saw. With the smell of paint still fresh in the flat, I suffered again, this time from two attempted burglaries in the space of just 48 hours. On the first occasion, someone (or two or three for all I knew) tried to kick my front door in. It meant untold hassle in getting it repaired and strengthened. I had to fight, really fight, for what I considered to be minimum security requirements.

The second was discovered by me by accident. I had been tossing and turning in bed for several hours the following night and felt so uncomfortably hot I headed for the patio to cool myself down and get some fresh air. On arriving, I was horrified at what I saw. A spade and an iron bar had been left propped up against the corner wall; a plant pot had been knocked over and its contents carelessly abandoned on the flagstones. I quickly looked to my right and saw that someone had hacked out the wood from the french windows leading into my kitchen with the aim of removing the glass. They hadn't quite succeeded. Maybe they had got scared and left quickly, thinking they'd been heard or spotted. It meant yet another call to the police. They should have installed a hotline for me.

There was more to come. Three times during the following week, I was cruelly disturbed in the early hours of the morning when someone would press my doorbell intercom and a young male voice would ask if a certain person was in. On each occasion I scrambled out of bed and raced to my bedroom window in an effort to establish the identity of my tormentor. But whoever it was had already disappeared.

The motives for doing this, I decided, either stemmed from the desire simply to inflict distress, or else to assess — for sinister reasons — whether anyone was present in the flat.

And then before the week was out, these were followed up by the most sickening incident of all. I was sitting in my lounge, when I suddenly had a feeling I was not alone. Most of the time such sentiments are purely imaginary, but this felt different. I looked down the hallway. Through the letter-box two eyes were peering out of the darkness at me. I was the object of someone's undividedly prying attention. It was like something out of a horror movie. I was disgusted. Again, the police were alerted.

All this additional harassment inevitably proved injurious on both a physical and mental level. Getting to sleep was proving almost impossible again. My ears became alert to every little sound – the creak of furniture in the night as the rooms grew cooler, the whistling of the wind around my flat, the rustling of the fallen leaves outside.

For a while I adopted a deliberate policy of taking – or trying to take – some extra sleep in the afternoon so that I had more energy to remain on watch at night. What a terrible state of affairs to have reached! I knew it at the time, but it seemed I had no power to alter my course. My internal clock was becoming well and truly confused.

I borrowed a heavy walking stick to keep by my front door, and I wouldn't have been afraid to use it in a slightly more aggressive manner than that for which it was invented. I also resorted to sleeping with a hammer under my bed and, when awake, to switching lights on and off periodically to give the impression to the outside world of someone's presence in the flat. Call me paranoid, but they seemed sensible precautions to me, all to make me feel safer and to deter the kind of person I don't want watching over me.

I also urged the housing association to view as priority the establishment of extra locks on my french windows and metal plates on my new front door. I had, of course, changed the locks immediately after the burglary. The housing association admitted to there being some severe design faults in the new building in which my flat was housed and these obviously had serious repercussions on security.

Realistically, the only way I was going to manage to stay in my flat without turning into an emotional and physical wreck by having my much sought-after alarm fitted. I arranged for some companies to come round to my flat to give me some quotes. We were talking a minimum of £500 for equipment, installation, maintenance, and monitoring. Life's never easy! What price peace of mind?

Since I did not have any savings I could use, I applied for a community care grant from the Department of Social Security to cover most of the cost. The application proved to be a rather long, drawn-out affair, painfully so at times, especially when the supporting letters of reference which accompanied my application strangely went missing at their office and I had to start all over again. It culminated in an interview on a morning when I woke up wondering if I'd actually been to bed at all. I made what for me amounted to a supreme effort in the circumstances to look fit and presentable, ready for an onslaught of questions and some detailed probing from the person quizzing me on my application.

It turned out to be rather different. Here I was, supposedly to be interviewed about my request for a grant to fund the cost of an alarm to improve my security, yet everything was being turned on its head. Taking sleeping pills and having counselling, as suggested by the interviewer from social security, was *not* the answer I was hoping to hear. All this did was to show me how shrouded in her ignorance of AIDS this woman was and how incapable of appreciating the complexities of my security dilemma.

"You can always move," came the second unhelpful suggestion, oblivious to the stress of moving for someone in my position. It was all too simplistic. Here I was, prepared to argue my case for an alarm but all the interviewer did was refer to alternative courses of action, all completely unsuitable. The urgency of my situation seemed to have been dismissed out of hand. I felt I was being rubbished and that it was a waste of time being there. The negative comment I was receiving grew positively antagonistic towards the end. I complained bitterly about her attitude, since it was extremely upsetting to have to go through such an ordeal, especially in full view and earshot of all the other applicants and visitors. This lack of privacy added to the frustration. She told me I would receive the results of my application in the post the following week. Another agonizing wait.

I returned home feeling absolutely wretched. I was convinced I'd be turned down. If they didn't award me a grant I'd just have to fundraise the money somehow, somewhere. (Anything involving gendarmes, though, was definitely off the agenda!) Unable to disengage my mind from the morning's dismal activity and feeling more and more that I had been treated much too unfairly, I telephoned the community care grant department and communicated to the manager the full extent of my concern. It was a difficult conversation, but an honest one. I simply had to lay my feelings on the line.

A week later I received a cheque in the post for the

amount I had requested. At first, I was disbelieving of the very piece of paper I was holding before me. Shocked, startled, surprised, I was none the less extremely grateful. Some good came out of it, after all. *Thank you.* They had bought me some peace of mind.

Or had they? The alarm company exceeded my expectations by saying they were able to come and instal it and have it in full working order in just the one day. I asked them to start the work right away. The fitting created a small amount of mess — mostly plaster dust from all the essential drilling and banging. My neighbours must have thought I was building a boat, but it was an inconvenience I happily put up with, knowing that by the end of the day I would have the security I had longed for. My worries would be over. My alarm was linked up to the police, so I felt doubly at ease when I was out of the flat. Soon afterwards I had a metal security plate fixed to the front of my door to lend additional strength. There was no way they could get into my flat now, I thought. But it didn't stop them from trying.

I came back one evening to find several large, dirty footmarks up my door and bits of plaster on my carpet inside from the impact of someone kicking it. The incident was repeated three more times in the space of four weeks. Over and over again I asked myself just what I had to do to make my home secure and stop whoever it was from damaging my property. I no longer felt the guilty party to be an opportunistic burglar. Such a person would have been dissuaded from trying his luck once the alarm was fitted. It seemed as if it were the same person, though. Since the alarm would sound after any forced entry there seemed little to gain from repeated attempts, except, perhaps, a malicious sense of enjoyment in inflicting damage on one person's flat. I wondered if it was some kind of vendetta. Why me? Why my flat, despite my security measures?

Determined not only to keep the burglars out but also to stop them damaging my front door further – each kick weakened the frame a little bit more – I decided I would deny them any further access, so I had a customized metal gate fitted to my door.

Fighting the good fight with all my might seemed to have become the story of my life. I checked on the funding possibilities with my housing association and was led to believe that help could be given. The next thing I heard was that I was *not* eligible for a grant for this kind of "home improvement". It seemed I had been let down again. My subsequent application to various charitable organizations all met with the same response: it was the responsibility of my housing association to provide me with a safe, secure home.

As things stood, this was clearly not proving to be the case and evidence strongly indicated they were reneging on their agreement – a service which I paid for. Further discussions with the housing association seemed to make them relent a little, though only by putting what seemed to be insurmountable obstacles in my way. I obtained an agreement from them that "they would fund the cost of the gate provided they bolted it onto the door surround" – this was apparently in order to comply with certain regulations. I was never given any information as to what these regulations were.

My impression was that they were stalling and

hoping I would forget the whole idea. Nothing was further from my mind. I contacted the gate suppliers, who were recommended by the local Police Crime Prevention Officer, and was informed that the gate had to be welded to the brickwork, not bolted as advised by the housing association. I seemed to be in a no-win situation. The gate company was unwilling to supply the gate unless it was welded, either by themselves or the housing association. The latter would not agree to carry out the welding, nor pay for the gate if they could not bolt it on. What an extraordinary state of affairs. What gives? And so the saga went on and on and on. Unable to await the outcome I decided to go ahead and order the gate and then battle to be reimbursed by the housing association. If the worst came to the worst, I thought, I would just have to borrow the money involved or sell something. I had to have that gate fitted regardless, for the sake of my additional security.

Certainly, it wasn't all doom and gloom. The Lift Appeal had been moving along steadily, despite my inability to commit myself fully to it during my periods of illness and tiredness over the previous few months, which had been caused largely by the problems I had experienced in my flat.

Then one day I received some unexpected news. Good news, in fact, though in touching circumstances. I was informed that a patient who had been cared for on Elizabeth Unit at Mildmay had left some money in his will specifically to fund the new lift. I could hardly believe it. When Claire told me over the phone, just a few minutes after she herself had received the news, I was speechless. We had reached our target in less than a year. I was on such a high. My mind flashed back to all the events we'd planned, all the money we'd raised and, of course, all the patients I'd spoken to on the Units. I naturally wondered about the identity of the patient who had bequeathed some of his money to fund the new lift. Never beyond my wildest dreams did I think we would complete the Appeal by obtaining a legacy. It was a sad reflection, but jolting myself back to the present, I could not help feeling extremely happy and very grateful.

"That's wonderful. What an amazing gesture for that patient to make. I can't believe it's actually happened . . . We've done it!" I continued to enthuse in a similar fashion for some time, although I didn't want to become too over-excited in case there were any problems or legal complications in sorting out the will. But to have been cautious at that time would have been somewhat boring in the light of such heartwarming news. We – and more importantly *I*, in view of my condition – had actually achieved something important. There would be a finished product at the end of it, as a reward for all the time and effort which had been invested. A definite case of light at the end of the tunnel (or the lift shaft!). It was well worth a quiet celebration.

The next stage consisted of employing a lift company to refurbish the old workings. Neither of us being technically minded, we were content to submit our ideas and thoughts to the people concerned and for me to offer a patient's perspective on the practicalities of using the lift.

In so far as the interior of the lift was concerned, though, the details were very much down to Claire and me. This was our project, after all! It was so good to be in control, seeing the project through from start to finish, and now we were discussing the interior design. It had heightened my sense of value within society and shown me I was still capable of achieving significant goals. The whole project illustrated to me how AIDS could prove a terrible handicap sometimes, by reducing my energy level and state of well-being, and yet I had managed to conquer the negative aspects, because of my stubborn enthusiasm to be successful and not let my condition get me down . . . at least not for long.

We were united in our vision for the interior of the lift. Right from the beginning, I had wanted to see something not merely functional and comfortable, but attractive and interestingly designed. In other words, I wanted it to be a pleasure for patients to use it.

What we needed to do was to enlist the help of someone we could trust to translate our ideas into action. Someone who would listen, understand and advise on the workability of it all. Someone with the freedom of imagination, to make additional suggestions compatible with our own. Someone professional. Someone specialist. Someone with an excellent reputation. In short, we gave the commission to an interior designer with his own company, the aptly named Inside Story. Based in Scotland, they specialized in kitchens and the designer jumped at the challenge of being able to do something a little different. He was hardly a novice at it, though. This lift would not be his first!

Having discussed our initial ideas with him, we waited for the plans to come through and liked what we saw. Clad in coordinating cool grey and soft mint laminates, incorporating various shadowgap strips in the design to create extra interest, the lift would feature two black uplighters and a light bronze tinted safety mirror at the rear. It would not have looked out of place in a luxury hotel. The low-level automatic operation would incorporate an illuminated panel to clearly indicate the lift's exact location at any time and thereby increase its user-friendliness. Special needs were incorporated in the design as a priority; for instance, a coated brass handrail and a black anodized aluminium nudge bar for wheelchair users – since the primary aim of the lift was to serve the patients, it having been funded, planned and developed especially for them. *That* was the idea at the outset. Only time will tell . . .

SIXTEEN

In and Out of the Shadows

The common cold has a lot to answer for. In a normally healthy person it poses few problems, but give it to a person with AIDS and it can wreak havoc, especially on a depleted immune system.

Common cold or not, it was common knowledge that there was an excessive number of viruses going round this winter and, *en route* for countless other unwilling victims, they decided to take temporary refuge in me.

For eight long hard days I battled with the symptoms and wondered how much longer it would go on for. (Temporary refuge? More like a sitting tenant!) On the ninth day I woke up after a night of repeated tossing and turning, feeling worse than ever. I shifted position in bed, which immediately alerted me to the fact that my whole body now ached and I felt totally washed out. The sheets were soaked with sweat and sticking to me as readily as clingfilm. The close-on-tropical humidity inside my bed made me fling the bedclothes to the floor in an effort to reduce the temperature of my immediate surroundings.

This small, insignificant physical exertion only increased my pounding headache, which seemed to worsen on any movement, not unlike a migraine. And I could feel the pit of my stomach bubbling and gurgling and grinding uncompromisingly which, combined with a singularly acid taste in my mouth, brought on a severe state of nausea. This was a respiratory disease raging out of control.

Alarmed at the intensity of it all, I visited my GP, optimistically thinking that I'd just be dispensed some antibiotics and confined to bed for a few days to allow them time to flush the toxins out of my body. It wasn't to prove as straightforward as that.

"Hello Michael, so how are you feeling at the moment?" the doctor started.

I didn't even respond. I knew that my symptoms and mounting distress would speak for themselves. Words would have been superfluous.

"Your temperature's very high — I don't need a thermometer to tell me that," she said, but none the less inserted one in my mouth for good measure. She then donned her stethoscope and asked me to breathe in and out while she listened to my chest. She needed to repeat the procedure. The worried look on her face did not escape my attention.

"There's something I'm not happy about in your right lung, Michael. It needs to be checked out more thoroughly. As a precaution I'm going to arrange for you to be admitted to hospital. It's best to catch these things early, I'm sure you understand." The alarm bells in my head started ringing loud and clear. "I'm worried about . . ."

"PCP," I interrupted. She nodded, demonstrating some degree of concern.

Pneumocystis carinii pneumonia — PCP for short — was an infection of the lungs caused by an extracellular parasite of uncertain status. Small children, immuno-suppressed patients and people with HIV infection were particularly susceptible.

"There's no time like the present so I'm going to ring your doctor at the Westminster to explain the situation." A bed was duly reserved for me.

I packed an overnight bag, called a taxi and in the intervening ten minutes made a few phone calls to close friends. I couldn't help wondering if this heralded the start of something I didn't want to know about. *Pneumocystis carinii* pneumonia had a horribly onimous ring to it. In my state of weakness I resigned myself to being ill. During the taxi journey my frame of mind degenerated so much that I even started thinking about death.

On arrival at the Westminster I was warmly welcomed by one of the nurses, which helped to ease the tension, if temporarily.

"Hello, Michael. We knew you were coming. The room's all ready for you. We'll get the doctor round straightaway. Perhaps you'd like a cup of tea in the meantime?"

Left on my own, I sat in my room looking around the four walls rather monotonously, asking myself whether I would get out of here or not. I was grateful that the doctor came in at this moment. His entrance shocked me out of my misery. He explained to me that he needed to perform some tests, one of which was to measure blood gases — that is, to ascertain the amount of oxygen in the blood. It involved the insertion of a huge needle in the artery located in my groin. His famous last words were: "Don't worry, it won't hurt."

I shouted out in pain, then slowly accustomed myself to the suffering.

X-rays were taken of my chest and lung area and these immediately showed up a couple of shadows on my right lung. My GP was right to be concerned. But what were they?

More blood tests were taken. More tea and sympathy were offered. And the results of the tests were revealed to me extraordinarily quickly.

"Well, Michael, it looks as if you can go home." I must have looked stunned at this unexpected turn of events. "You've come through absolutely fine. It doesn't look as though there's anything seriously wrong and there's no need to keep you in overnight. However, with these shadowy areas showing up on your right lung in the X-ray we still can't rule out the possibility of PCP until some further tests are taken. For these you'll need to go to the Kobler Centre tomorrow and book yourself in as a day patient."

The next day couldn't come round soon enough. The last time I visited the Kobler Centre was when I received my AIDS diagnosis, following identification of the presence of oesophageal candida. I wondered what they'd find this time.

First of all they studied my shortness of breath. I had to pedal away on an exercise bicycle for several minutes. I then had to give an induced sputum sample. A tube was placed in my mouth, the other open end being connected to a machine full of chemicals. I was asked to breathe in the noxious substance, which forced me to cough from the bottom of my lungs, as opposed to the shallowness of my throat. The resulting sample of sputum was immediately removed for testing, although the analysis would not be ready for another week. Another week of worry, not knowing if anything was wrong, not knowing for sure if it was the start of PCP. Even if the results came out negative, one final test remained — a bronchoscopy — to eliminate beyond doubt the presence of PCP in my system.

I don't know how I survived that week. Although I had good reason to be optimistic — everything had proved negative so far — my mind was not at ease. My fears ran riot. I had one anxiety attack after another. And yet I told myself amid all the confusion that if it were PCP and it was detected in its early stages, the prognosis was extremely good. It could be cured.

I hardly went out at all except for essentials like milk and bread. I hardly saw anyone. There was good reason. I wanted to avoid catching something else to add to the mayhem of what I already had. This was something I had to see through, live through, largely by myself. And I know I wasn't my normal self on the telephone.

For a whole week I raided my freezer, eating foods that I'd prepared for a rainy day, and I was grateful that I'd had such foresight. I was only interested in meals that were quick and easy to prepare. My sleeping was erratic. I'd wake up in the middle of the night sweating profusely, then get out of bed and wander around my flat to cool off, generally at three or four o'clock in the morning. I was having to change my bed every single day during that week. Hugging the duvet into the cover was a major exercise. I kept myself awake worrying about it all. Chatting to friends on the phone just provided a temporary lift. I'd then revert to my former state.

And then I received the test results. They had come out negative, which was a source of relief, but it meant I had to be booked into the Kobler Centre again for a bronchoscopy, scheduled for the same week.

The "day of the bronchoscopy" soon came round. I had been asked not to eat or drink anything after eight o'clock in the morning. This was to ensure an empty stomach by my two o'clock appointment in the afternoon. Needless to say, I was starving hungry and desperate for a cup of tea by the time I arrived at the now familiar surroundings (though I wish they weren't) of the Kobler Centre. My cousin Alice was not going to work that day and offered to accompany me to the centre. It was like a repeat performance of the day she journeyed to Mildmay with me for the first time for my referral for respite care.

I was asked to undress and put on a white robe. I rallied myself for what was to be the most important test of all and which would put an end to the worry of not knowing. Whatever the result, I told myself, I knew I would be able to cope better. Good news or bad news, at least I would then have something to act on. I knew the procedure that lay ahead. A general anaesthetic was administered to relax the muscles before a long tube with microcamera attached, was inserted through my mouth and down to my lungs. The camera was used to investigate the shadows revealed in the X-ray and relay a moving picture back to a monitor. The whole test was apparently completed in five minutes.

When I regained consciousness my first reaction was to ask whether they had found anything suspicious. The doctor advised me that, unfortunately, the conclusive results of this test could not be confirmed until the evening of the following day.

"If you ring in at about six o'clock, we should be able to let you know."

"Oh, OK then," I muttered, still somewhat drowsily, in a casual sort of way, as if my future, my life, hardly depended on it.

Having been delivered to my home by taxi, I headed straight for bed to sleep off the effects of the anaesthetic. I felt as limp and lifeless as the three week old lettuce I'd forgotten lay lurking in the salad compartment of my fridge. And in terms of lettuces, three weeks is positively ancient.

From five o'clock to six o'clock the following evening all I remember doing was watch the minute hand tick round. Will it be OK? Won't it be OK? Will it be OK? Won't it be OK?

I made the phone call. "Kobler Centre. How may I help you?" came the reply. ". . . oh, just a minute Mr Kelly, I'll get your notes."

An anxious, long wait ensued – probably only ten seconds, but it seemed like ten minutes. Did this mean it was bad news? Perhaps they were stalling because they didn't know how to break it to me.

"Here we are. I have your results in front of me. You'll be pleased to know the test came out negative. There's no PCP. Have a nice weekend."

So that was that. I phoned friends and we shared in the relief together. It appeared that I had suffered an unusually bad cold which had got into my chest and lungs and sent out some rather confusing warning signals. Providing I took the antibiotics which I had been prescribed, the condition was expected to clear up in a few days.

Two days later I received a letter from the Kobler Centre informing me that a pneunonia-related growth had started up in one of the test cultures. I telephoned them for more details, but they were unable to provide any, except to reassure me that my pneumonia had nothing in common with PCP and was most probably just a by-product of the cold which I was now shaking off. None the less, it was something that needed to be eradicated from my system. I was advised to continue with the antibiotics until the end of the course and, since only a few days' supply remained, I would soon know if the drugs had proved ineffective.

I had to make sure I didn't develop a temperature and become short of breath. It was a case of having to monitor my condition very closely. I was not out of the woods yet.

I had been looking forward to an opportunity to celebrate a return to what for me amounted to good health, but was cruelly stopped in my tracks. Now there was something else I had to fight off. The combined effects of the physical symptoms, the emotional stress, the unpleasantness of the actual tests, the need for yet more tests, the prolonged wait for some of the results and the announcement of the good news juxtaposed with the revelation soon afterwards which indicated I had not yet been given the "all clear", produced their inevitable delayed reaction. In one word: depression.

In search of an antidote, I realized I still needed a positive assurance that everything was OK and, until I received that, my mind would not be at rest. As an extra precaution, therefore, I arranged to see my doctor at the Westminster.

"Hello, Michael, it's good to see you. How have things been?"

"Not so bad I suppose, considering, but I'm a bit worried about some of the tests I've had." Deep down I suppose I just needed the extra assurance that only a qualified doctor who actually knew the history of my condition could give me. After swiftly putting my mind at rest, he changed the subject.

"By the way, Michael, I've got some other news for you. I don't know if you've heard it on the grapevine – you know how quickly news spreads round here – but I'm going to be leaving the Westminster. I've obtained a senior post at another hospital."

"Yes, I did know, and was sorry to hear it. I'm pleased for you, of course, but I'm sure your patients will all miss you."

"You could of course see another doctor here – I know you see the consultant every now and then – but the whole department's moving next year. We're amalgamating with St Stephen's. You may therefore prefer to start going somewhere else."

I mentioned that I could perhaps see a doctor at the Kobler Centre, having already been treated by a couple of its doctors and therefore didn't feel like a stranger there. I had no real desire to start from scratch in terms of having to detail my case history.

"We can arrange to have your notes transferred over

to the Kobler Centre very easily, if that's what you decide," he concluded. I wished him good luck. He wished me well. We both meant it.

I had been closer to the edge than ever before. But I found that, as I gradually got rid of my cold, I was becoming more empowered inwardly, and returning to something like my former self. I couldn't remain in the depths of despair forever. "I'm going to bloody well fight this," I gestured in a mood of self-incitement as I studied the sad, drained face I saw in the mirror.

Still staring at myself and beyond myself in the mirror, as if in search of the psychological essence of my being, I scorned the exaggerated affects a cold could have produced on my condition. I was well aware that such a positive reaction, borne out of a mixture of something approaching bravery and a fair sprinkling of self-effrontery, signalled my continuing improvement.

At last I was edging closer away from the danger zone – the unremitting darkness that AIDS can bring when fuelled by an uncompromising bout of illness. Indeed, it had taken much longer to recover from this particular episode and I had been delivered a sharp reminder that AIDS was always there, despite the remission periods. But recovering I was. After all, Christmas was just around the corner and I was starting to look forward to the idea of celebrating it. I had cards to send, presents to buy, arrangements to make.

I didn't count, however, on waking up on Christmas Eve with conjunctivitis and then, four days later, receiving the news that my Granny had died. It meant, of course, an unscheduled visit to Scotland to help sort out her affairs and offer support to her other relatives, especially those older ones for whom the idea of attending to all the practical details would have increased their emotional and physical frailty. The fact that I had no money to get me up to Scotland was beside the point. I couldn't *not* go, out of respect for my Granny, so I borrowed the money.

Sure enough, Wee Sadie, the kindly old soul that she was, would be sorely missed. She had graced her own small part of the world for nigh on ninety years. Her generosity of spirit had known no bounds, most memorably when I was a child and was allowed on countless occasions to escape the storms of my own house for the calming shelter of her little cottage. It was only three miles away, but for me it had been a world apart. I now considered it an honour to ensure that the final journey to her resting place at the side of my grandfather was made with the dignity she deserved.

The knowledge that her spirit had been laid to rest instilled a calm and a peace in me, too. The memories of my childhood bound up in her would be pleasant, comforting ones. I took a look at myself. My eye infection was clearing up. And in the meantime, my energy, for some time dormant, had been vibrantly reawakened on account of all the rushing around in Scotland I felt it was my respectful duty to perform.

It may have been winter outside, but in my heart it was suddenly spring. I was pulling through. I thanked God.

Postscript

AIDS must be one of the worst diseases ever to *in*fect and *a*ffect mankind. At its most destructive it can hold you in a vice-like grip and not let go until it's torn you apart bit by bit, weakened your defences, eroded your ability and your energy to think positively, and reduced any vestiges of self-esteem to a pulp. This accounts to nothing less than personal tragedy.

For *Living on the Edge* I've gone back in time and dredged up feelings, emotions and experiences long since buried, and can assure you that no enjoyment was to be had from it. These have been painful memories to relive, excruciatingly so at times. It was like being wounded and then constantly having the sores forcibly reopened, with the result that they're never allowed to heal fully.

But I've done it for a reason.

I'll never be able to right all the wrongs, but maybe someone, somewhere will benefit from this record of how I have coped, living with this terrible condition. Maybe that someone is *you*.

I do not like forced preaching or aggressive dogma, but I just want to be able to challenge, even if indirectly, people's misconceptions, prejudices and judgmental attitudes around the issues of HIV and AIDS. More